CHILD IN A BOARDING-HOUSE

Also by Jean Donaldson:

Innocents to Everest

CHILD IN A
BOARDING-HOUSE

Jean Donaldson

**ILLUSTRATED BY
SHEILA DONALDSON**

UNITED WRITERS
Cornwall

UNITED WRITERS PUBLICATIONS LTD
Ailsa, Castle Gate, Penzance, Cornwall.

British Library Cataloguing in Publication Data:
A catalogue record for this book is
available from the British Library.

ISBN 1 85200 060 0

Printed in Great Britain by
United Writers Publications Ltd
Cornwall

To my mother

Inside me, I quickly come to the barrier,
the limit of what I am, beyond which I
cannot go by myself. It is such a narrow
limit and yet for years I thought it was
the universe. Now I see it is nothing.

Thomas Merton

Used by permission of the publishers.
From *The Sign of Jonas* by Thomas Merton,
published by Sheldon Press in 1976.

CONTENTS

Part Two

FOREWORD

It really is *odd*, when your own home is full of
boarders. What my Dad calls the Inmates. Which
isn't fair, because some of them get to be sort-of-
half-family.

But they're always moving on. Some stay and
some go. In a boarding-house, nothing stays put,
except the rooms.

Sometimes you feel that a house starts at the
top, suspended by its roof and hanging in the
clouds. Anyway, the top is a good place to live,
with all the rest of the house happening underneath you. *But* . . . people are not the only things
that live up the top . . .

PART ONE

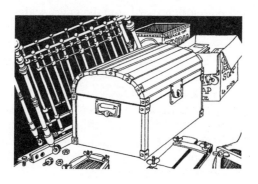

1

THE PLACE AT THE TOP OF OUR HOUSE

I'm eleven years old and I'm not stupid. My brain knows it's not dangerous in there.

So why am I standing outside the door, taking a deep breath before I dare to open it and go inside this room we call the Tank Cupboard?

It doesn't matter how often my mother says, "Be a good girl and run and fetch such-and-such from the Tank Cupboard!" I always run and fetch it in the same way . . . whizz up the three flights like greased lightning, get to the door . . . and stop.

I always stop for a second and listen to two sounds. One is my heart bumping. And the other is this sinister whispering that goes on all the time behind the locked door.

The key is stiff and I turn it . . . clack! . . . and the door creaks open onto the black nothingness of this room without a window. And the whispering becomes a loud hissing and bubbling of water, furiously fuming away to itself in the darkness.

A frightening sound . . . a scarey menace.

I hate it.

*   *   *   *

I didn't have to say it like that.

I could have said, "At the top of our house there's a room where we keep the cold water tanks."

But then you wouldn't know how I feel about it.

I'm not just pretending that I find the tanks scarey. I really do. But I don't know why. It's like when you get spooky feelings in dark passageways. You know it's silly, and the sensible part of you isn't afraid at all, but another part is scared to bits and has bad dreams about it.

That's how I am about the tanks.

The Tank Cupboard itself is all right. It's just a largish room full of interesting junk and all the things there's no place for anywhere else in the house. Also a few important things like the bed-tightening spanner.

So I'd better explain about that first.

It's Sheet-Changing Day and it's the holidays, so I'm helping. We'd nearly finished. We'd done our beds, and Mr Ashley's, Mr Sprigget's, Mr Grüning's, Miss Elphin's and Miss Fazackerly's, and had only Mrs W's left to do. But the minute we started, it creaked and wobbled. My mother tested the big nuts and bolts that hold the bed together, and finger-tightening wasn't going to be enough. So that was that.

I said I'd fetch the special spanner from the Tank Cupboard. My mother said, "There's a good lass, only don't get too dirty, will you?" because she knows I usually end up a bit cobwebby from climbing over things and exploring. Then she said, "No great hurry, I'll have to start the lunch first."

So she went off to the Kitchen and here I am.

Mrs W, by the way, is the guest in the Downstairs Bedroom at the moment. She hasn't been here very long, and I hope and *hope* she doesn't stay for ever and ever. The other boarders are all right and some of them are very nice indeed, but I can't think of anything good to say about old Mrs W. So I'm not going to say her name. If you knew her you'd understand. She is just totally amazingly incredibly awful and bossy and selfish, and goes red in the face and nearly blows up when she gets angry, which is quite often.

My mother looks after everyone, and wouldn't want anyone to

16

have a wobbly bed, but least of all Mrs W. She is very old and heavy and fidgety and if her bed collapsed I hate to think what might happen. Even if she wasn't hurt, she'd probably burst with fury.

Anyway, to go on from where I'd got to, about me and the tanks, and the hissing and bubbling in the darkness . . .

I'm standing here with the door unlocked and opened. I know where the switch is in the dark and I reach up and put it on, which provides what my father calls A-Little-Light-On-The-Situation.

You can see now, that this is a proper room with a high-up ceiling and yellowy distempered walls. And away up the other end across the jungle of junk, are the two water tanks. They are a deadly grey like battleships and very high, a lot higher than me.

The one on the left has rivets all round the edges and is closed in. But the one on the right is open at the top and the water is very deep and totally black. Floating on top of it is this old copper ball-cock thing that hisses and goes up and down all by itself like something alive. The water goes down, down, down like letting the bath out. But then it starts coming up and up and up, and maybe one day it isn't going to stop but will come right over the top.

Why is there no window?

It makes you wake up in the night and think stupid things, like that the tanks are so dangerous they have to be completely shut up and locked in, in case of what they might do if you let them free. Such as filling the whole house up with a flood. The sort of stupid thoughts you only have at night.

And that is plenty enough of how I feel about them.

In the daytime I don't mind a bit of scariness. In fact it's quite enjoyable. If it doesn't go on for too long a time.

Some people might think it a waste to have such an interesting tank of water that you can actually get at, and not make use of it. For instance, it would be good for some kind of experiments, like seeing how long a sponge would float before it sinks.

However, there are disadvantages. One is that the scariness would go on too long. Another is the water being so deep. I tested it to find out, but I couldn't touch the bottom and got my jersey sleeve wet even though it was shoved right up to my shoulder.

But the main disadvantage is *me*.

I'm just too law-abiding which is a pity, but it's how you come to be if you grow up in a boarding-house. That is, if it belongs to your parents. You have to be fairly polite and reasonable and seen-and-not-heard. My mother has enough to do looking after the guests, without me being a pest.

Come to think of it there is another difficulty, and that is reaching up to the tanks. The last time I tried, my feet had grown too big to fit onto the wooden frame the tank sits on. I had to stand on top of the Dressing-Up Trunk, which is a cabin trunk with a rounded black lid. I'd just started having a good look into the murky depths when there was a crunch and my feet began to go through the trunk lid. I hit my chin on the edge and tore my skirt and had to jump down in a hurry and not tell.

The truth is, I only did it to dare myself.

I was quite glad not to stay any longer, so close to all the hissing and bubbling, and the angry water fuming furiously and wanting to get out.

So there's no point in pretending I'm not scared of it, because I am. But that is not the sort of thing you tell anyone about, as they wouldn't understand.

The Dressing-Up Trunk is small compared to all the other stuff in the Tank Cupboard. In the middle it is mostly boxes and trunks, including another one with a cracked humpy lid which Miss Mole left behind. It's full of blue exercise books with her writing in. I had a look but didn't read any, partly because it's grown-up scribble and an awful bother to read, and partly because you're not supposed to.

Nobody actually tells you that you're not supposed to, but you're not.

The tennis rackets for the summer are there in wooden presses with wing-nuts at the corners, and somebody's old bicycle, and the box with the Christmas-tree decorations. Also a flat double piece of polished wood with metal bits, called a trouser press, though I've never seen it used. My father puts his between the mattresses. On the bed, that is. Not the mattresses here in the Tank Cupboard.

The mattresses here are the lumpiest old ones, but otherwise they are the same as the ones on all the beds, made of grey-and-white material with leather circles stitched on to keep the stuffing in place. They lean along the walls against the spare beds. The bed heads and feet are made of black painted iron rods with brass knobs. They also have big iron sockets that stick out and are really bad for hitting yourself on when you climb past them. The bases have bouncy metal meshes in an iron frame with holes at the corners for the nuts and bolts. The special spanner for tightening them is hanging on the wall, and I have to climb over things a bit to reach it.

Which I'd better hurry up and do.

And switch off the light and lock the door.

And whizz downstairs to Mrs W's wobbly bed.

But I'll tell you something about this top landing, before I go.

Outside the Tank Cupboard door is a dark and cramped place with only just about enough room to turn round. On your right is where ghosts would live if there were any, behind the hanging curtains on clattery rings, where spare coats and suitcases lurk in the shadows.

But if you turn round and take two paces across the top of the stairs, you come to a little square landing which is light and airy. It's a lovely dizzy place to be. You can lean right over the top banisters with your head hanging down and your hair hanging down, and feel what it'd be like to be a bat with everything looking different upside down.

It's also a good place for a yo-yo. And even better for my bat with a ball on elastic, as you can zoom the ball out into space without hitting anything.

Places are so different. Two paces from dark deadness to light lifeness. Every landing and every room in our house is like a separate world, or like going to a foreign country or something. I mean, with a different look and a different feel, and different people living in them.

There are three steps up again, from the top landing.

But I'm not telling about them just yet.

However, in the dark spooky bit there is another door, next to the Tank Cupboard door, and it leads to a bedroom.

19

2

THE ROOM NEXT TO THE TANK CUPBOARD

The Room Next to the Tank Cupboard is the smallest of the rooms that boarders live in, and at the moment it is Mr Ashley's. The people who stay in it have always been men up to now, and youngish, perhaps because of it being at the top of the house with three lots of stairs to run up. They don't stay very long, maybe only a few months, not years like the old ladies. I suppose that's because they're on their way to somewhere else.

Quite often they're handsome and nearly always mysterious.

Mr Hughes was tall and agile and wore a leather coat and goggles and roared off somewhere every day on his motor-bike that he kept down by the dustbins. Every morning he'd slip downstairs like a dark stranger, wheel the bike out, pull the goggles down, roar and - off! Once when he was cleaning it he said, "Want a ride? Hop on, then!" and I was glad he didn't have his slippery coat on, because when he zoomed round to come back I'd have fallen off if I hadn't had a good hold of his jersey.

Then there was Mr Muller who was mysterious but not handsome. He was short and solid and worked in some kind of industry but then he had to go back to Germany. The only interesting thing I can remember about him was the night he came in after everyone was asleep and he was . . . you know, drunk . . . and made an awful lot of noise trying to find his way upstairs.

And there was Mr Dupré who was French and had a stupendous number of phone calls at the weekends, which it was my job to run and answer if I was nearest to the Front Hall. I'd race up the first two flights of stairs and shout, "Mr Dupré! Phone!" and then get out of the way quickly so as not to get knocked over. He always crashed out of his room and flew down four stairs at a time, sliding his hand down the rail and swinging round the corners the way I do only more so, took one leap across the hall, listened in to the receiver and sang out; "Oui! . . . Oui! . . . Toot sweet!" crashed the receiver back on the arm and leapt back upstairs three at a time, humming happily.

The next thing you had to do after that was be very quick and put back all the stair rods before what my Dad called the Repeat Performance. This was when he zoomed down again a few minutes later with his best jacket on and his hair all slicked down and scenty, and looking pleased. Except the once, before we knew about putting back the stair rods that he'd knocked out, and the stair carpet came undone all the way down so that it was just one long straight piece, and Mr Dupré did the most amazing gymnastics and landed in a heap at the bottom, muttering things in French.

This made my Dad, who had put his head round the Dining Room door to see what the noise was and if help was needed (which it was), give a secret smile and sing a favourite bit from one of his operas, that ends 'Chacun à son goût' which is French for 'each to his own taste'. I know that's what it means because I asked him and he told me. He quite often has little smiles and makes musical comments, but that's the only time he has ever told me the meaning of any of them. It was Miss Fazackerly, by the way, who is one of our old lady guests, who called them that. She looked down her nose and said quite sharply, "And what does *that* particular musical comment mean, may I ask?"

But my father didn't tell her. He just went away quietly. If I ask him something, he goes silent while he considers whether to tell. If he decides not to, nothing can change his mind, and if I nag, he is more likely to say, "Go and boil your head!" or else, "Oh, go to

Potiseliukum!" But I don't know what that means, and sometimes he just says, "Oh, go to Pot!" for short.

I should explain why it was the Dining Room that my father put his head round the door of. The reason is that, at meal times, the guests sit with us at the big dining table with a white cloth and napkins, or have their breakfasts there while we have ours in the Kitchen. But when it isn't meal times, the Dining Room belongs to us, the family, and the guests go in the Lounge.

Another thing is, to say what I meant about my father's operas, not that he writes them, but he sings in them. That is his job, in the opera chorus at Covent Garden, which is why he is often here in the mornings, but has rehearsals in the afternoons and perfor-mances in the evenings, and is sometimes away on tour to Manchester or Birmingham or even Edinburgh, where he got me my little silver brooch like a dirk with cairngorm stones in. Opera singing was my mother's job as well, until she had to stop because of having me.

However, my mother does not make musical comments, partly because she is too terribly busy to think of anything like that, and partly because she's too kind. And she never tells me to go and boil my head. My Mum always explains things if she can.

You might wonder why I sometimes say 'my mother' and 'my father' and sometimes 'my Mum' and 'my Dad'. The reason is that I actually call them 'Mummy' and 'Daddy' but that looks too silly for words, if you write it, so I shall just put whatever seems best. I have a cousin who calls his parents 'dear', but I'm too shy to do that, even though I would quite like to.

Anyway, to get back to the Room Next to the Tank Cupboard. At the moment it's Mr Ashley's room. Mr Ashley has been here just a few months and is tall and thin, but quiet and gentle, a pleasant person with pale fair hair and long fingers which must come in useful because he is a dentist.

The reason I know he's a dentist is this. I had to take up a parcel that had come for him, and that he had missed noticing because it was underneath the hall table, not on top with the letters. So I ran up with it and knocked on the door two or three times, and called out, "Mr Ashley! Parcel!" just to make sure, and as there was no answer I thought I would open the door and take it in and have a quick look round. Not to touch anything, but to see what was new, just for a second, before he came back from the bathroom or wherever he was.

In the room there has always been a cupboard like a chest of drawers underneath with a china cabinet on top, with two glass doors. On the bottom shelf of the cabinet I could see two big piles of yellowy-gold magazines and, right at the back, a dark object that I couldn't be too sure about.

I was so busy goggling through the glass that I didn't hear him coming. The amazing thing is this. Instead of doing what they all do, and going, *"What are you doing?"* he just laughed and said, *"Do you want to see my skull?"*

Well, I'd thought that was what it was, and I was right. He took it out and let me hold it and showed me the way the teeth go, and explained about needing to study it for being a dentist. It was very interesting, but not nearly as interesting as the magazines, which I was longing and longing to get a look at.

In the end I managed to blurt it out, "Please, what are the magazines?"

He got one down and showed me. Here are the Facts:

1. They are called the *National Geographic*.
2. They have a list of Contents on the cover.
3. There are about sixty, all different years.
4. His uncle left them to him, in his Will.
5. He said, "Borrow them any time you like!"

Mr Ashley said *that!* To *me!* And that I might take two at a time and come and change them on my own, as long as I don't touch anything else and as long as I knock on the door first, and wait, in case he is there and in case he says, "Hang on a minute."

They are like a stack of gold ingots in a dark room, only they are more precious. Quite a few pages at the front and back are funny advertisements from America, which I like reading, especially the Campbell's Soups ones. But in between are the most incredibly marvellous photographs of all the most beautiful and fascinating things in the world, as well as plenty to read.

Up to now I've read nine. One was from twenty years ago in 1918, with pictures of nurses tending wounded World War soldiers in France. But my best so far have been:

1. Tropical fish, especially Angel Fish, on coral reefs.
2. Photos of things called Plates, from a book about ferns

23

and mosses, showing the tiny delicate moss flowers down below, and the fern patterns above, with brown spores.
3. Volcanoes erupting in Hawaii, taken at night, all black and red and gold with molten lava like rivers of fire.

I hope Mr Ashley stays a long time.

However, considering it is the Room Next to the Tank Cupboard, he maybe won't.

It is a Dark-in-Three-Ways room. One, is being next to the awful furiously fuming dark water hissing and bubbling in the Tank Cupboard, and the spooky bit outside the door behind the rattly curtain where the ghosts would live if there were any.

Two, is because out of the window you can see nothing at all except bricks which is the huge high side of the next door house, unless you lean out and look down into our side passage which is like a canyon with the dustbins down the bottom.

And three, is that when you lie in bed there's a door *up above your head* and behind it is a black hole. You can hardly believe this, but it is a proper door that you can walk through, if you balance on top of the bed-head and turn the key, and step into the dark. Which I did, once, with my torch. But there's nothing there. Except sometimes when you're trying to sleep you can hear the wind whee-ing and whoo-ing behind the door.

The one glorious and treasurey thing in the room is the curtains. They are very dark blue like a night-time sky with gold and red tulips. Some of the tulips are the right way up and some are upside down. Sometimes if you keep looking at them you would think the upside down ones are parrots hanging on trees in the jungle.

You might wonder how I know about all this. The reason is that once upon a time, when I was too big for the cot in my mother-and-father's room, this was my room for quite a long while. But when Mr Hughes came to live in it, and then Mr Muller, and Mr Dupré, and now Mr Ashley, I went to live in the Linen Cupboard, but I'll tell about that later.

It is strange, remembering. You think you have forgotten, but things pop into your head. I have remembered four things about when I was in the Room Next to the Tank Cupboard.

*   *   *   *

To begin with I got tucked up and the light put out. But when I was a bit bigger and allowed to read in bed, it was a nuisance in winter going across the cold lino to turn off the light. So I fixed up a sort of string arrangement from the head of the bed, up over one of the hooks in the ceiling above the light bulb, and then onto the brass knob of the switch by the door. It worked quite well, unless the string broke. And you could only turn it off, not on. It was also useful one summer when it was so hot at night I could hardly breathe. I tied a wet flannel onto the string, near my face, so that I could flap it and make a cool breeze.

My mother is a contralto, and has a very beautiful voice. Even when she is speaking, or calling to me, it has a singing sound. Sometimes she stood beside my bed and sang me the same song her mother, my Devonshire Grannie who used to live with us, sang to her when she was little. It goes:

> 'Jesus bids us shine with a clear, pure light,
> Like a little candle burning in the night.
> He looks down from heaven to-oo see us shine,
> You in your small corner, and I . . . in . . . mine.'

Just sometimes she would kneel down by my bed and say the Lord's Prayer with me. But she was too shy to do it unless I asked specially. She can't do it in the Linen Cupboard, even if I asked, because there isn't room.

And there was also the time when Tigger died. He was my dog that I had from Granpie, who is my father's father who lives in Acton and comes and takes me out, and is my friend. We had been looking at puppies in the window of the pet shop along past Ealing Common and then went to his and Acton Grannie's house for tea, and after tea he drew a picture of a terrier pup in my autograph book, and underneath he wrote:

> 'This is the dog we've seen today
> If ever funds ran to it,
> Might someday p'raps belong to you,
> With mutton bones and suet.'

25

b

But I didn't think he really meant it, until he came to our side door with Tigger, who was a wire-haired terrier, on a red lead, and said he was for me. I expect my mother got a bit of a shock, too.

Well, it is too long ago to get sad about now. But at the time it was very sad indeed, because although I loved him and played with him in the garden after school, he got ill and lay quieter and quieter in his basket, and died of distemper, in spite of all the vet could do and in spite of all my kind mother did to nurse him.

And then she said, "Now don't go crying for Tigger all night, darling, because he's all well now."

You know how it is, when someone says something like that. Even if you hadn't thought of doing it, you wonder if perhaps you're supposed to, so you start. And thinking about what they have said makes you want to cry, anyway. And once you have started you can't stop, but go on and on until you don't know whether you're still being sad or only being sorry for yourself, because of being in such a mess, with a wet pillow and hurting eyes and all bunged up and not able to breathe or swallow. If you try to swallow, your throat sticks together at the back, which is very scary. Because if you can't swallow and can't breathe, what is going to happen to you? So you try hard to do what they always say, pull yourself together, and stop crying and go to sleep. But after a bit it starts again all by itself, and in the end, if you are little, you start going, "A-hoo! A-hoo!" really loudly, hoping that someone will come.

So that is how I remember what room I was in at the time, as I howled all night in a pretty spectacular way. At least it felt like all night.

Actually we were all of us sad, and upset that we had not known how to look after him properly, especially my father, who loves dogs and had an Irish Terrier when he was a boy. But his had been tough, not a pedigree. And we all vowed never to have another dog, because no one could take the place of Tigger.

The last thing I remember about living in the Room Next to the Tank Cupboard is something which perhaps people do not talk about. Certainly my family never ever breathe a word about such things. But if I am being truthful I should say it.

It was when the bed had been moved round so that it was not

26

any longer under the Door in the Wall leading to the Black Hole, but had its head in the far away corner so that I was looking at the two pictures over the fireplace and at the night-sky-blue-with-parrots-in-a-jungle curtains that were closed for bedtime. When you are little, you go to bed while there is still light in the sky, enough to show up the curtain patterns, even when there is only a brick wall outside.

And then the patterns get paler, and go grey, and then it is dark.

That was when I started thinking about Space going on and on for ever. I still think about it, but not so much.

I used to lie there, trying to work it out till I got dizzy, like when you shut your eyes and twizzle round and round and round and then have to stop because your head is going round and round and you can hardly stand up any more.

There's the night-time sky out there, and the moon, and all the planets and us going round the sun, the way we drew it at school, and there's the Milky Way and the galaxies, and in between and out beyond there's all the blackness of Space going on and on . . . till what? Till not anything. Because it keeps going on and on and on. But how *can* anything go on and on without getting to an end? Yet it *does*, because that is what Space is. But what does it *mean* - 'on and on'? I can't find any picture in my mind to tell me what it means.

It's the same with Time. And Eternity, like in the hymn where it says: Through all eternity. And I know that God *is*, but . . . *how?* How can there be somebody who has been there always? What does this 'always' *mean?* How can there be somebody like God unless somebody made him first . . . but that doesn't make sense. And if there wasn't God, then who made us?

I really do remember how I used to lie there making my mind go back and back and back and back and back, until it nearly burst. But I never told about it.

Perhaps everybody does this. And perhaps someone understands. But how can I know, if they don't talk about it? It's a whole lot more interesting and important than, "How did you get on at school?" and, "Don't forget to say 'Thank you'!"

That is all there is to say about the Room Next to the Tank Cupboard.

3

A PLACE CAN BE MORE THAN ONE PLACE

Up three steps and you are in my mother-and-father's room. It is a room in the sky, a room up in the clouds, the highest room in the house.

It is higher than the two big may trees, one pink and one red, that grow on either side of the grass and nearly meet in the middle. And it is higher than the old apple trees that my Dad says used to be an orchard where the bottoms of all the gardens are now.

When you lie down, you see sky and nothing else at all except for the Virginia Creeper curling up over the sill and down from the roof.

Everything in the room is light and pale, and the light of the sky shines from it. The furniture is goldy-coloured, not polished, but with the wood patterns showing. The curtains are thin like paper, and creamy-coloured with the flower patterns nearly washed away, so the light of the sky shines through them. The walls are white distemper but the ceiling is papered like wallpaper, with white and silver square patterns that you can lie and look up at and count, and make them into other things like big squares, or diamonds, or even tram lines running from the corners of the room and crossing in the middle, according to how you make your mind see them.

This is very useful if you have the measles or something, because this is the bed you have it in. At least, I do. So as well as sitting up and doing puzzles or painting on the bed-table that Granpie made me, I can lie down and do sums with the ceiling.

Anyway, to get back to the room. The big bed gleams in the light, because all the bits you can see are made of shiny brass rods with square sides, and the big rods at the corners have knobs like pyramids, that unscrew. Where the brass rods are supposed to join the long curvy one that goes across the top, they don't. You can see about an inch of the black metal rods that are inside them, which makes it nice and jangly because of them being so loose.

On the bed, first there is the mattress that has a big hollow so that you roll down into the centre. Then, sheets which have been sides-to-middled or patched or else are like tissue-paper and your toes go through. Then, a lot of thin blankets (because of Best-for-Boarders) with black lines at the top and red blanket stitch edges. Then an eiderdown. And on top of everything comes the bed-cover, which is so white it is blinding.

It is made out of a linen sheet with a starched white edge about a foot deep, crocheted by Devonshire Grannie who lived in the room under this one, and it is all daffodils and daffodil leaves and grasses so real you would think they were growing, only frozen in snow.

When the sun shines it is as if the light bounces on the bed and hits the ceiling and comes back again onto the brass and the whiteness.

On the right of the window is a washstand, the same as in all the rooms, with a swirly grey-and-white marble top and a white basin and jug. And on the wall above is a wooden medicine cabinet which has carved ivy growing up the front of it, as real-looking as the creeper creeping over the window-sill.

On the left of the window is the dressing-table where my mother sits to brush her hair. It is set across the corner so that the huge big mirror shows mostly sky and a swallow flying in from outside. Really he is a paper swallow stuck over a crack in the bottom left-hand corner of the mirror, but he looks real when the clouds are blowing, and he is a beautiful dark blue with red under his chin.

There is no other room in the house as high as this.

There is no other room at all like this.

I lay on the floor one day when the clouds were blowing and when the swallow was swooping across the airy sky spaces, and the room started moving, too . . . whirling and birling along. I really think sometimes it could take off and fly in the sky.

I will tell you a thing that I thought about.

A place can be more than one place.

There is a room in our house. It is the highest room. You go up three steps to it. It is my mother-and-father's room and it is a magic cave of darkness.

There is no window. All the corners are black. But there is a golden glow, and big dark shadows walking on the walls.

We are not all separate, them in the brass bed and me in the cot and my baby brother in the cradle. We are all in the big bed together. Everything is black or orange or golden and it smells like Christmas. There is a candle alight by the bed and we are tucked up in the middle, propped up on the pillows. My mother is peeling a very big orange and making it into cloves and sharing it out, and my father is making shadow pictures for us.

A rabbit and a swan and an eagle and an old man smoking a pipe.

The rabbit is the best.

The rabbit is just about as big as the room, and it climbs up the walls and waggles its ears and winks its eye. And we blink our eyes in the stingy smell from the orange peel. The candle flame blows sideways in the wind under the door, and the wax spills over and makes waterfall shapes down the side of the candle, and my baby brother gets put back in the cradle and I get put back in my cot-bed and watch my mother climb back into the big bed in her old cotton nightie.

With her night-time plaits hanging, and her old nightie that hangs down straight, she looks like a big pale tree moving in the candle light.

Then the cave goes dark.

That was a long time ago.
But I was remembering it and thinking about a place being more than one place.

There is a room in our house. It is a long way up the stairs. I stomp up the last three steps. It is my mother-and-father's room and I am fed up with it.

Granpie comes behind me, carrying the tray with my lunchtime dinner. I can smell, all the way up, that there is spinach on the plate. I hate spinach.

He puts the tray down and unfolds the little card-table with the green cloth top, and puts a chair for me and a chair for him and tucks a napkin into my neck and says, "Be a good girl and eat it all up and I will read to you." I eat the potatoes and the scrambled egg and I eat bits of spinach, very slowly and horribly, in between. There is no point in not eating it, or I shall have to sit there till I do. So I am good, and he reads the story about Lop-Ears, who is the rabbit in *Fairyland Tales* that Granpie and I get every week.

Then he puts me in the cot, which is in the corner and is beside the big brass bed except that there's a cupboard along the wall in between. He pulls up the side of the cot and fastens the catches and tells me to lie down like a good girl. He fetches his chair and sits beside me and sings *Guide-Me-O-Thou*, very softly and gently, with his little pointy grey beard going up and down, and his old grey cardigan over his grey waistcoat with the gold watch-chain across it.

Guide-Me-O-Thou is his hymn that he whistles through his teeth when he is fixing loose door-knobs and things like that. But if you sing it, it goes:

> 'Guide me, O thou great Redeemer,
> Pilgrim through this barren land;
> I am weak but thou art mighty,
> Hold me with they powerful hand.'

31

Then he says, "Be a good girl, now, and go to sleep." And he goes away to have his lunch.

I stand up again and do not know what to do. It's like this every day. I don't want to be in a cot and I'm too big for a cot, anyway, and I'm not sleepy. How can a person go to sleep in the middle of the day when the sun is shining? I want to go out in the garden. But if I'm not good, then everything will go wrong, and I won't get to do interesting things later on, and everyone will be miserable, especially me. So I bounce up and down for a bit and then have a look round to see what there is to see.

At the foot of the cot is the gas-fire that is on in winter, and the huge high fireguard like a lion cage, except when it has clothes hanging on it to dry. And next to that is my mother's dressing-table where she brushes her hair. She undoes the night-time plaits, with her fingers twinkling down very fast like playing the piano, and then brushes and brushes and brushes. She has beautiful brown hair, so long she can sit on it, but then she plaits it up again and winds each plait into an ear-phone and fixes it on each side with hairpins.

On the dressing-table, as well as the crochet mats, there is her round hand mirror and her brush that have black wooden backs, and a green pot with a lid, for the hairpins. And an orangey-coloured cardboard box with a lid, with little pictures of powder-puffs all over it, that has her face powder in it. And there is a king-fisher pot with a fat yellow tummy and greeny-blue wings and head and an orange beak. My mother combs out her brush when she has finished, and winds the long hairs into a little circle, and lifts the kingfisher's head and pops them inside.

That's all I can see.

But there is nothing to *do!*

I pick up the book that Granpie has left in the cot for me to look at. But I've looked at it so many times already and there aren't many pictures, and only of a goose with a bonnet on. It's a very small book . . . but nice and thick . . .

That was a very, very long time ago.

But I remember it because of what I did.

I got so furious that I tore every single page out of that book and then tore each page into very small pieces, crying all the time, and stood up and threw them over the side of the cot, all over the floor.

It is quite startling to think that it was really me, doing a thing like that! I could never have imagined it in a million years, because if there is one thing I really love, it is books.

But it makes me remember how many different places a place can be . . . a sky room . . . and a magic cave . . . and a prison-because-of-my-mother-being-so-busy-in-the-Kitchen.

4

WRIGHTIE'S ROOM

I'm just on my way upstairs with Miss Elphin's breakfast tray . . . butter and marmalade, triangles of toast with the crust cut off, milk jug, small brown teapot, and her napkin rolled up in a bone ring, all on a best embroidered tray-cloth. Also a bowl of horrible Shredded Wheat, like a slice cut off the bathroom loofah.

The tray isn't heavy but it's awkward because things slop so easily. When I reach her room I have to balance the tray on my knee while I let go with one hand to knock on the door. Then open the door and grab the tray again quickly and try not to jiggle it.

So it's not my favourite job. And I must admit Miss Elphin isn't exactly my favourite sort of person. But she's been here so long, my Dad says she has taken root, so I can't leave her out.

And anyway, she lives in Wrightie's Room.

So here goes.

Miss Elphin sounds like the name of someone pretty. In fact she's

34

weedy and wishy-washy, all fawn and beige, and is like the White Queen in my copy of *Alice* that Granpie gave me, with wispy bits of hair hanging down, and a shawl pinned up all anyhow and trailing sideways.

She is old. Not very, very old. But old, and the room smells all stuffy. I have to put the tray down and fix the pillows behind her back, then hand her the napkin and wait while she arranges it over her bed-jacket and the top of the sheet, and then put the tray in front of her. And then hold it steady again while she shoves a bit of hair up under her hair-net.

Miss Elphin is, I am very sorry to say, always too droopy and miserable-looking to smile. I don't think her mouth *can* turn up now, it's too much out of practice. But at least she says, "There's a good girl - thank you!" in a moany voice.

I used to try cheering her up, like saying, "I think it's going to be a nice day." But it didn't work, because it made her think how it would probably rain later.

So now I just shut the door quietly and gallop down the two lots of stairs, and swing round the big newel post and down the three more steps and past the Cupboard Under the Stairs and along the passage and into the Kitchen, and have my breakfast and off to school. My Dad is still finishing his and reading a library book, which is a thin yellow one, so it's probably a Western about Hop-Along-Cassidy, as he likes those best.

That's funny, when you think about it, because that is a bit how my Dad walks, like Hop-Along-Cassidy, because of having been shell-shocked in the War. He is quiet, and tall, and bony, and one leg drags just a little, so he makes it walk faster by going dot-and-carry . . . sort of hop-along, hop-along.

My Mum will have her breakfast later, if she gets a minute. Otherwise she'll have it what my Dad calls 'on the hoof'. At the moment she is busy doing a big cooked breakfast to take into the Dining Room for Mr Grüning, who doesn't go to work. She did the cooked breakfasts for Mr Ashley and Mr Sprigget earlier on, so that they could get away. After Mr Grüning has finished, Miss Fazackerly has her cereal-and-toast breakfast in the Dining Room, as she is a brisk sort of person even though quite old, and wouldn't dream of having it in bed. Last of all, my mother will take Mrs W's breakfast-in-bed. I'm only glad I don't have to.

But I always take Miss Elphin's before school, because of my.

Mum being busy then and because it is a long way up all the stairs.

Well, as I said, Miss Elphin lives in Wrightie's Room. She comes down to the Lounge later on, of course, but the room she sleeps in is Wrightie's Room.

You might wonder why it is called that, and not Miss Elphin's Room. The reason is, because Wrightie was the first person to live in it, and stayed a long time, long enough for me just to remember always saying, "Can I go to Wrightie's Room?" and running up to sit on her knee and get told stories. Her real name was Miss Wright but I called her Wrightie. She was there so long and was so much like one of our family, that you can't think of it as anything else except Wrightie's Room.

That reminds me of a story, which is a true story that my mother tells.

Once upon a time, when my mother was very little, a gentleman came to their house and wanted to see how well she could count. There in front of them, open on the table where her own Mother (who is my Devonshire Grannie) had been sewing, was her workbox. Along the top little compartment was a row of reels of coloured cottons, and a thimble. The gentleman pointed along the row with his finger, touching each in turn, and getting my mother to count. She counted, "One, two, three, four, five, Mother's Thimble!"

Because that is what it was. It was not 'six', it was her Mother's Thimble. So no matter how the gentleman tried, not even if he promised her a sweetie for counting to six, she wouldn't do it, but went on counting, "One, two, three, four, five, Mother's Thimble!"

So you see what I mean about calling it Wrightie's Room.

We are not stupid about it, however. For instance, if I happen to be around when the enamel hot water jugs are being carried up to put on the wash-stands, my mother might say to me, "Will you take that one up to Miss Elphin's room?"

But . . . if that room and another one were both empty, with no one staying in them, and a new boarder called Mr X was coming and we asked where he was going to go . . . would she say he was going in Miss Elphin's room? Certainly not!

36

She would say, "We'll put him in Wrightie's Room."

Because that is its name.

If you stand on the top landing by the yo-yo place and the spooky bit by the Tank Cupboard, and go down ten stairs, you arrive at the floor where most of the guests' rooms are. There are two big spacey ones that look out the front onto the road, and Wrightie's small one which is sort of at the back.

The reason I say 'sort of', is this. Our house is what is called L-shaped. The top of the L is the back of the house. It sticks out into the garden and has three floors, with my mother-and-father's room at the top, the Kitchen at the bottom, and Devonshire Grannie's Room (that is Miss Fazackerly's now) in the middle. And in the short bit that is sort of at the back, the bit that doesn't stick out, there are just two floors, Wrightie's Room at the top, and the Dining Room at the bottom, with French windows and steps down into the garden.

Wrightie was a walnutty little person who wore brown and gold woolly clothes and had a wrinkled face and twinkly eyes.

Once upon a time, before I can remember, there was a ring at the front doorbell and my mother hurried along the hall to open it, wiping her floury hands on her white apron, one of the ones she makes out of sheets that are too old to patch, and are stitched and starched with a belt and a bib and a big pocket, like a nurse's apron.

At the door was a little old gypsy woman with a big flat basket covered with a cloth, and an old black hat like a man's hat squashed forward over her eyes. She had bits of hair straggling down, and in her dirty old hand she held out a little bunch of violets. She squinted up at my tall mother and smiled a crooked smile, showing stumps of teeth with gaps between.

In a wheedling voice, the gypsy said, "Buy the pretty flowers, lucky lady, for you'll not be sorry, and you have a kind . . . Oh! . . . Oh! . . ."

And she began to sink down on the step, one hand clutching at the ragged shawl over her heart.

My mother felt frightened, but she helped the old lady inside to sit on the hall chair and went away to fetch a cup of water. When she came back she found the black hat thrown down on the floor and a pair of wicked old eyes, that she knew very well, twinkling up at her. It was Wrightie!

Such a shock did this give my mother that it was she who had to sit down and have the drink of water, while Wrightie stood there naughtily gleeful, rubbing the black stuff off her teeth and saying, "April Fool! April Fool!"

My mother hugged her and scolded her and forgave her, and Wrightie kissed her and pinned the bunch of violets on her apron, and that is the end of the story.

I was too little to remember this. But I think I knew that she was a naughty lady and we all loved her. Anyway, she was my friend who told me stories, and my kind Mum says it made her a bit sad to think it was Wrightie who had the time to do this, and was so good at it that I was always asking to go to Wrightie's Room.

Well, it wasn't only the stories.

There was a nice squashy cane chair by the gas-fire. And either side of the fire was a little square picture of a gnome with a beard, playing whistle tunes to the birds. In one, he is sitting on a grassy bank and playing to the chaffinches and robins and in the other he is standing by a fence with a blackbird on it, and he and the blackbird are doing a duet.

And there was Woofy, a brown china dog who stood on the mantelpiece. The shiny stuff on the china is thin in some places and thick in others, so that some parts of him are pale gold and some shadowy brown, making him look really alive. And he has his head on one side and a wicked eye like Wrightie's, looking up at you from under his lop ear.

The reason I am saying '*is*', about Woofy and the pictures, is that they are here right now, in my room in the Linen Cupboard. And those were the pictures that I mentioned being over the fireplace in the Room Next to the Tank Cupboard. Because Wrightie gave them to me when she left.

I *think* she left to go and look after her brother.

I don't think she died, but you can't be sure, because my family are extremely funny-peculiar about anything to do with dying, and won't mention it, the same as they won't mention all sorts of other things.

I am not making this up.

The reason I know about it quite definitely is that when I was over at Granpie's and Acton Grannie's house last winter, he gave me a Girls' Annual, one of the good ones with plenty to read. Someone at school had already lent me a copy, but before telling Granpie this I had a quick look through to make sure the stories were the same, and they were. That was when I saw that the story called 'Best Blacks' was missing. It had been cut out very, very neatly, with scissors, leaving just enough paper so that the other pages didn't start coming loose.

'Best Blacks' wasn't a particularly interesting story, and there was nothing bad in it, but it was about a very grand funeral, and there was a picture of the prancing black horses with black plumes pulling the hearse with glass sides so that you could see the coffin.

It gave me a nasty shock. Seeing it wasn't there, I mean. I could picture Granpie sitting reading through all those schoolgirl sort of stories, just to see if there was anything I oughtn't to read, and then fetching the scissors and cutting four pages ever so carefully. And thinking I wouldn't notice. So I couldn't possibly tell him I had read the book, and had to say, "Thank you *very much*, Granpie!" the way you do, to show that you're pleased.

But it is not a comfortable feeling when that happens. Almost as if they were the child and you were the grown-up.

And that is the reason I'm not quite sure why Wrightie went away.

The only other boarders I remember in Wrightie's Room, after Wrightie and before Miss Elphin, were the Briony Boys and their mother, Mrs Briony. They weren't with us very long but they were the kind of people who stick in your mind. This is because:

1. They were the first exactly alike twins I had seen, about two years old and always dressed the same.
2. When their mother asked them, "Who's Mummy's little . . . ?" they both together finished the sentence by going "Brrr - Brrr!" I suppose she had taught it to them, but it was a pretty soppy party trick.
3. Mrs Briony had invented a wonderful game for wet days, and I shouldn't say anything against her because

it was so beautiful that I was very glad to be invited
to join in.

This is how it went. We all sat at a round table in the corner of the room, the twins kneeling up on cushions with their mother helping one of them and me helping the other. She put a clear glass basin of water on the table and brought out a whole new packet of birthday-cake candles and a box of matches. We lit candles and dripped them into the water carefully so that the wax drips made little rafts of different coloured blobs joined together.

When the raft was an interesting size and shape we took it in turns to lift it out and see what it looked like underneath, and I got to keep some and take them away in an empty matchbox.

In our family, even old candles are used again for the next birthday. So there was a very rich feel about it, as well as being so beautiful, with the water and the lights, and the rafts making shadows on the bottom of the bowl.

It is a strange thing thinking about rooms. They change so much when different people are living in them. If you think of the room when Wrightie was in it, you see fireside and chair. With the Briony Boys, you see the table, because it was a doing room.

But with Miss Elphin, it is just bed. The bed was always there but you didn't notice it. With Miss Elphin, you don't notice anything else.

For one thing, like Miss Elphin herself it always has extra bits draped round it to keep off the draughts. And then there's her having breakfast in it. And when you take her hot-water bottle up at night, it has to go exactly one third of the way down the bed, and you have to take her nightdress out from under the pillows and wrap it round the hot-water bottle.

But it is still Wrightie's Room.

Even if I don't remember her stories, I remember her. And Woofy sits on my shelf with his head on one side and winks at me from under his lop ear.

5

MR GRÜNING'S ROOM

The lamps are lit out in the road and the wind is blowing. The curtains are open, and the plane trees are flying their night-time leaf and branch shadows across the ceiling. There are glints of gold and strange snaky shapes lurking in the corners.

Big black branch shadows sway and swoop on the wall like dancing cobras. Then a wild whoop of wind swings the tree and lets the lamp-light through. It shines on red mahogany chests and flickers gold on the figures that sit all around the room.

I am lying here trying to think like poetry, and making word patterns.

I know what the figures are, though, from dusting them in the daytime. They are Mr Grüning's Hindu gods and goddesses, because of having been in India for so many years. Some have head-dresses, or snaky things round them, and one has lots of

41

arms, and another is standing on one leg. I tried to look them up in the Encyclopaedia at the library but it was too complicated and I can't remember which is which. The only two names I can remember, because they sound nice, are Shiva and Kali, so they will have to do.

They are all dull gold coloured and beautifully carved, and are strange but not interesting. Just there, not alive.

But . . . oh, the shadows, and the flickering light, the leaves blowing and the whistling wind.

Mr Grüning is away for a month. I don't know where he has gone. Perhaps to Bournemouth, or to stay with his sister. And I am in his room. It is the most totally fantastic amazing treat.

I try to be good, and sleep. But I can't. It's not just the shadows, or Shiva and Kali. It's the books, the Kiplings. I've only read the *Jungle Book*, because of getting it last Christmas, but Mr Grüning has every Kipling that there ever was, and I'm allowed to read them and I've only just started and I can't bear to stop.

My mother came up and said, "Put the light out now, dear, and go to sleep!" just when I had got to where Puck was saying that the People of the Hills don't care to be confused with painty-winged impostors. And then Puck says, "Butterfly wings, indeed!" and goes on about Sir Huon and his people setting off from Tintagel Castle in the teeth of a sou'westerly gale, with the Horses of the Hills wild with fright. That's the story called 'Weland's Sword'.

I take my torch out from under my pillow. I get *Puck of Pook's Hill* from the bookcase, and back into bed, and go on from where I got to.

> "... wild with fright. Out they'd go in a lull, screaming like gulls, and back they'd be driven five good miles inland before they could come head to wind again. Butterfly wings! It was Magic - Magic as black as Merlin could make it, and the whole sea was green fire and white foam with singing mermaids in it. And the Horses of the Hills picked their way from one wave to another by the lightning flashes! *That* was how it was in the old days!"
>
> "Splendid," said Dan, but Una shuddered.

Well, I wouldn't shudder, that is for sure.

But my torch has gone out. It's been getting feebler and feebler

42

for ages. The battery never lasts long, so that's that. I put the book carefully on the floor till the morning, and lie and think.

This room is on the same floor as Wrightie's Room but it's so different you would think you were in another house. It is not small and square and cosy, but long and tall and spacey, with dark shiny wood and mauve walls. It was always called the Mauve Room but now it is very definitely Mr Grüning's Room. A lot of the stuff is his, like the dark brown leather armchair by the gas-fire, and the rugs, and all these Indian figures keeping guard around the place.

They do not stare at you the way our picture in the Dining Room does. Their eyes are open, but either they are in a daydream or looking at something else. So they are peaceful, and not threatening.

All the same, the room is not empty. It is as if there were someone in it, maybe sleeping or breathing.

But they are nothing, compared to the books.

Mr Grüning's own bookcase is beside the bed. It is tall and elegant, and every shelf has a glass front which you lift and push up and back, so that it slides out of the way and you can see the books properly. Almost all are in red bindings with gold letters. They seem so full of life and they glow and speak, as if they were saying, "Come on, read me! What are you waiting for? I've got so much to tell you."

That reminds me - there's this other thing I don't understand.

It's not only rooms that are completely different at different times or with different people. I am, too. My outside is so different from my inside, it's like two different people. Not once, ever in my life, have I been able to tell anyone what I'm like inside.

For instance, about this room. I don't know why I am allowed to live in it while Mr Grüning is away. I just am. It is one of those things that happen if you live in a boarding-house. Maybe it keeps the room aired, or my mother wants to turn out the Linen Cupboard or something. Anyway, she brought me upstairs to knock on Mr G's door and ask his permission. She asked, and then we waited to see what he would say.

He wears a brown suit and smokes a pipe and is fairly old, but is tall and thin and very polite, even to children. So he put his head on one side, and spoke softly and musically, the way he does, dipping and ducking towards me as if I were an important guest in his house.

He said, "Yes indeed, a satisfactory arrangement. You will look after my room for me, won't you? You like books? Yes, I believe you do. Come!"

He showed me how to work the bookcase, which I've dusted before but never opened, and then he said, "Kipling is a great storyteller! Read any book you like . . . any you like! But start with *Puck of Pook's Hill*, and we shall see . . . mm?"

His face is thin and papery, but his eyes are all alive. I was surprised to hear him say so much. Because every day, with the guests and all of us, he is so polite that he only smiles and ducks his head and says, "Good morning!" and talks about the weather.

There must be so much more he could tell, if only he found the words.

I am even worse. All I can do is nod, or say, "Yes Mr Grüning!" the way I am supposed to, and shuffle my feet and be shy and stupid. It's difficult, living with people.

Books are different. Sometimes they tell you things that are very grown up, and that you didn't know and are not supposed to know, and that is very surprising and a bit of a shock.

But the best of all is when they tell you things you know already, things you didn't know anyone else knew, and you say, "Oh, yes . . . *yes!*"

It is as if the people who wrote them are saying, "I know you. And you know me. We understand about these things."

There isn't anything else to tell about Mr Grüning's Room, except that I'll have to hurry back from school and get my homework done and my shoes polished, and listen to Children's Hour on the wireless (because it's the next episode of Lost Worlds by Jules Verne with the thing that's going 'Thump! Thump!' through the jungles) and have my tea in the Kitchen and put the old ladies' bottles in their beds, and find another torch battery for after my light is put out, and go to bed quickly so as to get some more reading done.

*　　　*　　　*　　　*

44

I did. I put the proper light on, which is in a red shade with hanging bobbles and I sat up in bed so as not to hurt the book, and went on with Weland.

I like the page with poor old Wayland-Smith in his leather apron in the dark, but with the light of the fire spinning a pool of light round him and sparks flying up, and him squinting with his one eye down the blade of the sword and Puck blowing the fire while he hammers. But he is not a poor old smith at all, but one of the Old Gods. He is making the sword as a gift for Hugh the novice.

> He cooled that sword in running water twice, and the third time he cooled it in the evening dew, and he laid it out in the moon-light and said Runes (that's charms) over it, and he carved Runes of Prophecy on the blade . . .

There were shuffling sounds just now, and then a bump and a sigh, and for a moment I almost thought it was Kali coming off the chest-of-drawers to object to Weland, because of him being so much, much, much more real, but it was only Miss Elphin going into Wrightie's Room next door, to go to bed. And Weland and Puck went into the dormitory where the monks slept, and Weland put the sword into Hugh's hand and went and threw down all his shoeing-tools in the Chapel with a clang like suits of armour falling. And Hugh came out waving his new sword and shouting Saxon battle-cries and my mother stood at the door crying out, "Not still reading? Put the book away, darling!" and came over and kissed me goodnight and switched the light off, and I wickedly waited till it was safe and got my torch out and went on where the Abbot is talking.

> "Son Hugh, it needed no sign from a heathen God to show me that you will never be a monk. Take your sword, and keep your sword, and go with your sword, and be as gentle as you are strong and courteous . . ."

Ho hum! That is what I am *not* being, but anyway I can pretend that it isn't fair to have to try and sleep with Mr Sprigget playing a record on his gramophone, even though it is nice and soft, in the Blue Room across the landing.

So I kept going, and went on to where the story ends with Puck making them bite leaves of Oak, Ash and Thorn for forgetfulness, and with them not being able to explain to their father. Which is something I understand, because you never can explain.

"I see," said her father.

"Late - late in the evening Kilmeny came home,
For Kilmeny had been she could not tell where,
And Kilmeny had seen what she could not declare.

"But why are you chewing leaves at your time of life, daughter? For fun?"
"No. It was for something, but I can't azactly remember," said Una . . .

But perhaps they were lucky, and he knew anyway.

6

A BRAIN CAN BE MORE THAN ONE BRAIN

It's a Saturday today, and a lovely sunny and blowy one, so I've been helping with jobs that need a good drying day.

First was the front steps and brass - the brass first because of having to stand on the step to reach the bell. Polishing brass is easy, as long as you shake the Brasso tin hard enough so as it doesn't come out all runny.

But it's tiresome and fiddly.

Our front door is painted a beautiful dark green like holly leaves, with coloured glass in the top half, and a really handsome brass letter-box with 'LETTERS' engraved on the flap in curly writing. It also has a curly-shaped door-knocker across the front of it, which you have to lift out of the way with one hand while you polish the 'LETTERS' bit with the other.

But you can't.

Because the flap disappears inside, like posting a letter.

So . . . you . . . have to go *inside* the house again, and polish the flap sort of upside down, and then come *outside* again to do the rest of it, and not get polish on the green paint because it dries

47

white and makes a messy smear. Phew!

I forgot to say that before you start you take the outside door-mat and the huge big inside doormat out into the front garden and give them a good shake and leave them on the path till you are finished. And get the broom and sweep out any leaves or grit that have got onto the black-and-white tiles where the outside doormat goes, which is a very small sort of porch place between the two steps.

Then the bell. The brass bell on the right of the door.

It sounds easy - but it's so *complicated!* And maddening!

The bell is shaped like a small rounded pyramid with the bell-push in the top and lines engraved round its sides. I could reach it if it was where it's meant to be, on the outside of the wall.

But the bell is fixed onto a small square block of wood.

And the wood sits in a small square hole in the wall.

And it's loose. So I have to jam it tight while I polish.

The first time I tried, the whole thing disappeared backwards. I hurt my knuckles, hit the bell-push by accident, and my Mum came hurrying along from the Kitchen to see who it was coming calling.

She'd be expecting the greengrocer on a Saturday, but he comes to the side door. He is youngish, with pink cheeks and a flat cap, and holds his little blue Woolworth's notebook in his left hand, licks his pencil, and says, "What'll it be today?"

My mother chooses by looking in the big flat basket with the hooped handle. It has rhubarb leaves making a green frill, pink sticks of rhubarb and white celery and big golden parsnips sticking out sideways, and fresh peas and runner beans, creamy cauli-flower, crunchy cabbage, carrots and onions, and oranges, lemons, grapefruit and polished apples all nestling in the middle.

He writes down a long list, says, "Right you are, then!" and goes out to fetch it from the van. He brings it back in an orange-box and I help to put it away in the Scullery, which is where the side door is.

Once a year, the Breton onion man comes wheeling his bike down the road, with his blue French beret, and strings of onions hanging from his handlebars, and we buy some and hang them in the Scullery, too.

Anyway, to get back to doing the steps.

The steps are more fun than the brass. You fetch the white

enamel bucket of water, the whitening block and cloths, and do a quick wash to get muddy marks off.

And then the good bit, which is dipping the block very lightly in the water and smoothing it all over the top step, seeing if you can make it look all of a piece, and no patches. You soon find out, when it dries snowy white, whether you've missed bits.

Next comes washing the tiled part properly with a separate cloth, so as not to get whitening on it. And then have more fun with the bottom step.

I'd have experimented with practice patterns first, doing swirls and swoops, only:

It is Blanket-Washing Day and I had to go and help.

And:

Miss Fazackerly came out early to go for her sharp walk and said her usual sort of thing, like, "Earning your keep, I see!" and trod on the top step and trod whitening onto the tiles, which I know she can't help, because of taking little steps, but I had to wipe the tiles again.

And:

Mr Ashley managed to take a big stride over the whole lot, but stopped to say how was I liking the *Geographics*, and wasn't it a lovely day and the blackbirds singing.

Usually I'd have noticed the blackbirds.

But with things like the steps and the brass you have to do what they always say, keep your mind on the job.

It's as if your brain is having to go down a straight track, like railway lines, and can't go off to the sides.

Except that part of my brain knows that later on I'll be going over to Granpie's, the way I always do on a Saturday, and can swing on the swing or use his lathe, or maybe we'll make toffee, or melt lead in the ladle. But that is not my brain *thinking*. It is more like a hum going on in the background.

You have to keep your mind on the job doing the blankets or you get your fingers caught in the mangle.

That's my job, turning the mangle while my mother lifts the end of a blanket with the wooden tongs, then holds it with her

c

hands, spreads it, folds it once and again and feeds the folded end into the rollers. The hot water runs back off the blanket into the dolly-tub in steaming waterfalls. The apron end of the big zinc dolly-tub is shoved up close to the mangle, and my mother heaves the blanket bit by bit out of the suds, keeping the folds going all the time, while I ease them into the rollers with my left hand and turn with my right. The blankets come out the other side magically neat and pressed, and fold themselves down into the zinc bath on the concrete floor of the Scullery, ready for us to carry it between us out the side door and down the garden and hang them on the line.

It sounds simple. But it is a *huge* job.

First my mother has to change the blankets on the beds, according to which blankets' turn it is to get washed. She sews a Roman Numeral with red wool in the corner of each blanket to show what year it got washed in.

The dolly-tub has to get filled with buckets and kettles of hot water, then soap to make suds, then the blankets of which you can only do a few at a time - and then the dumper!

The dumper is a copper thing with holes round the bottom edge, on the end of a broom handle. It is pretty interesting to use, if you squish it down on the clothes or whatever in the tub, and lift it up slowly - slowly - till it slurps out with a squelchy sound and all the little holes have fountains of water curving out of them.

However, to go on and on and on, and then let them soak while you do something for the dinner, and then on and on again (which is what my Mum was doing while I did the step) is not much fun, especially as it's a lovely blowy day outside but hot and steamy in the Scullery.

I don't think there can be anyone else who has a mangle like ours, with wooden rollers and a gigantic green-painted iron wheel with a handle, and a wooden stand that is getting a bit wobbly and you have to shove your foot against it to stop it from walking. The only friends-from-school's houses I've seen so far have neat little white mangles with rubber rollers, on the side of washing machines.

So Blanket-Washing Day is maybe unique, but not much fun.

Anyway, we're finished now.

My Mum said, would I like to shell the peas while she did the potatoes? So we sat in the garden on the seat and did them together, and listened to the blackbirds and smelt the may trees, only she says we ought perhaps to call them hawthorns, as they did in the country when she was a girl. Only they are so tall, we call them may trees, as they come out in May.

Then I asked if I could do the salt before I went off to Granpie's, as it is my special thing, and you can only do it when the salt jar is nearly empty.

If my Mum had needed more salt after I was away, the block would have got chopped up in two seconds flat and into the jar before you could say Jack Robinson, and I'd have missed my chance.

So that is what I'm doing now.

Putting the salt block on the pastry board, carefully, so as not to damage the nice square sides. Taking the paper off. Getting the bread saw, because it's just perfect for tunnelling with.

I start at one end and dig a hole, put the knife in and scrape it round and round, and round and round, and round and round. Turn the block on end and tip the salt out and scoop it into the jar out of the way, and go on making the hole bigger.

Soon it is a cavern. The trick is, to go on until nearly all the block is cavern. A big cave, with thin salt walls all round, that the light shines through.

Thin like paper and sunlight filtering in. Maybe an ice cave in the Arctic. Or an under-sea palace made of thinnest delicate white coral.

Then when it's time to finish - chop, chop, chop - and the caverns crumble quickly like the tide undermining a sandcastle.

Now, there's a funny thing!

The minute I started on the salt, tunnelling away round and round, my brain got off the tram lines and went off in other directions.

No, that's not right! It didn't go off zig-zag, jumping from one place to another. It was thinking lots of different things all at the same time.

Now, how could it do that? There's a puzzle. How? It

51

couldn't!

But it *did!* I was thinking:

1. About scraping carefully, so as not to break the walls.
2. About it looking like a real cavern, and snow caves, and so on.
3. About how much time I'd got to spare, to do it in.
4. About the fact that the blackbird had stopped but the thrush had started, going, "Judy! Judy! Try again! Try again!" and that by the sound of him he was probably on his favourite place, the very top of the gable above my mother-and-father's room, straight up above where I was sitting in the Kitchen.
5. About the fact that my mother was making pastry for steak-and-kidney pie, up the other end of the table.

All those things were like real thinkings, and on top of all that, at the same time, my brain was:

6. Kind of dreaming through all I've done this morning, starting with shelling the peas and how good they taste raw and what a lovely scent the pea-pods have, and working backwards through the blankets on the line and the steam in the Scullery, to Miss Fazackerly stepping on my clean steps, and wondering why she has tittuppy feet and can't take a proper stride.

That's *six* different layers all getting thought at the same time! I just don't understand. *How* does one brain think all those thoughts at once without them all getting jumbled up? Do we have more than one brain, or something? Or does the brain have lots of compartments, like flats all being lived in by separate families?

But if it does, why couldn't I think all those things while I was polishing the brass? If my brain had gone floating off then, like going up and down in a lift, I'd have bashed my fingers, rung the bell, and got Brasso all over the green paint.

Well, perhaps somebody knows the answer. But I don't.

*   *   *   *

I cleared up, and made sure all the salt was off the board and into the jar, which is a beautiful pottery pot with what my Mum calls lugs, and is a shiny brown outside and a shiny grey inside, and used to be Devonshire Grannie's long ago.

Then I gave a little laugh to myself, without meaning to, and my Mum looked up from making pastry leaves to decorate the pie, and smiled and said, "What was that about?"

Very often I just have to say, "Oh, nothing!" or make up something, if it's too complicated to explain. So it was nice to be able to tell her for once, what it really was.

I laughed again, and said, "I was thinking about me doing the steps, and that made me think about Nellie. Do you remember the drawing Mr Sprigget did after dinner, that Sunday lunchtime?"

My Mum laughed too, but then pretended to be a bit shocked and said, "Now then! He was very naughty! Poor Nellie!"

Oh, well . . . it was nothing much, really. But Sunday dinner is about the only time we see much of Mr Sprigget, with him being out at his business, so we don't know him very well, only what he looks like.

He is not as old as Mr Grüning but not as young as Mr Ashley.

He is small and neat and brisk, like Rabbit in the Pooh stories.

At Sunday dinners, he doesn't usually say much, but listens a lot. His eyes look from one to the other, as if he is taking it all in and is a bit amused.

However, on the day my Mum and I were remembering, when we had finished the pudding course he reached into one of his inside pockets, took out paper and pencil, drew something and passed it round the table.

Everyone said, "Oh!" or "What *can* it be, Mr Sprigget?" except Mr Grüning who said it was a pipe case, because he has one just like it, for his meerschaum pipe. But Mr Sprigget shook his head, said, "A coffin for a one-legged man!" and drew something else.

This time, nobody guessed, except I said it looked like a beehive, because it did. The old-fashioned rounded sort, with a very tiny little door at the bottom for the bees to go in and out. Only I couldn't understand why the door seemed to have a dividing bit down the middle.

He took it back, put it away neatly in his pocket, and said,

"Nellie cleaning the front step!"

After about two seconds' silence, Miss Fazackerly snorted down her nose and said, "Tch - tch!" at the same time as Mr Grüning chuckled quietly and other people said, "Oh, Mr Sprigget, how *could* you!"

People are very surprising!

I expect I am a bit slow about these things. In fact, I hate to admit it, but I had to get my mother to explain it to me later. Things are so obvious when someone gives you a clue.

Nellie comes twice a week and is a Grand Help because she does the Heavy Cleaning. And Nellie is fat, and shaped like a cottage loaf balanced on short little legs. She likes to do the steps from inside, kneeling on the doormat, leaning out over the tiles with her head lower than her bottom. So it's quite true. That is absolutely all you would see from behind, a huge round hump and the soles of two tiny feet.

Now why didn't my brain notice that?

How does it sometimes think six things at once, and other times it goes to sleep?

7

THE BLUE ROOM AND WHAT COMES NEXT

The Blue Room is supposed to be the best room. As well as being tall and spacious it has a bow window and an extra little room called the Dressing Room, with a connecting door and a washbasin and a small balcony over the front porch.

Myself, I'd just say it was the biggest and poshest. Not my favourite. Well, the pale blue walls are a bit cold-looking. And Mr Sprigget is so neat and tidy, the place doesn't have any special feel . . . there's nothing of his own stuff in it, except the gramophone. And a few businessy papers and magazines.

My brother and I had the Blue Room once when we were in bed with the Whooping Cough. It must have been when we were very little. I only remember it because of the awful whoop-whoop noises we made, and because it's the only time I ever had a real nightmare.

Great black things with wings and grinning teeth came swooping at me down tunnels in the night. That was bad. Even more horrible was when they stopped swooping and just sat, silent and heavy and dreadful, all around the ceiling, and gaped at me. I shot bolt upright in bed, staring and pointing high up into the corners, one corner after another, shouting with all my might, "It's *there!* It's *there!* It's *there!*" and my mother came running.

Before Mr Sprigget, we had an English family who had just come from Brazil, and stopped in the Blue Room for a little while. I don't really remember them, only the story. We thought they must have lived in Brazil all their lives, because:

They asked my mother what she served for breakfast. When she said, "Porridge, Bacon and Egg, and Toast and Marmalade," they said they would have that. But when it came they put it all in the porridge - bacon and egg and butter and everything. How horrible! My mother went to clear the table and there they were, all sitting there and saying, "We're so sorry to leave it, but we didn't like it very much!" So she fetched them some more and showed them how to eat it. They were all right after that.

It's time to leave the landing with Wrightie's and Mr Grüning's and the Blue Room, and go on down to Devonshire Grannie's Room, where Miss Fazackerly is.

Flights of stairs have differences, the same as rooms.

The top flight is the best for sliding down the banisters, because you don't meet anyone except Mr Ashley.

The long stairs down from Miss Fazackerly's to the front hall and the downstairs rooms, you could almost call Stately Stairs. Because people come down them in their good clothes, to go out, or to sit in the Lounge, or to go to dinner in the Dining Room. And they don't rush, except for me and Mr Dupré, when he was here, galloping up and down to the telephone.

But the middle flight of seven stairs that I'm going down now, ought to be called the Stairs You Don't Want To Get Caught On. Everyone on the top two floors *has* to use them, not just to go out, but to get to the Upstairs Lavatory and the Bathroom, which are both on the same level as Miss Fazackerly. There are more people buzzing up and down those stairs, for one reason or another, than anywhere else in the house. Sometimes popping out of their rooms and slipping down the stairs quickly, at night, in dressing-gowns.

It can be very odd.

We had an extremely strange lady once called Mrs Barron. She was tall and straight and fierce like an eagle. I met her on those stairs once. It was daytime and she was in her proper clothes. I said, "Good morning, Mrs Barron!" very politely, and tried to pass her. But she stopped, and stood even straighter, staring at me. Then she said in a loud, haughty voice, *"One ought not to speak to one when one is going to the lavatory!"*

I think she was mad.

When you stop to think about it, there's something pretty extra-ordinarily peculiarly strange about living in a boarding-house, and it is your *own home.*

Mostly I don't think about it at all.

If I do, it's the other way round.

The way *we* live, is *normal.* But the way friends-from-school live, is so strange it's like a foreign country and talking another language. I went to Pamela Graham's the other day after school and saw their neat little flat, with a three piece suite round the fire, and everything new, and peaceful . . . and just for her and her parents!

I can't in a million years imagine what it's like.

Not that I want to live in a flat. I'd hate being so shut in.

We keep chickens. At least, my Dad does, it's his special thing. When he goes down the garden to feed them very early in the morning, and stands there on the grass in his old brown dressing-gown with a cord round his middle, his face all happy, and a dish in each hand and chickens all round his feet, he looks like St. Francis.

That's a funny thing too, because his name is Francis Henry. But he is called Frank. My mother's name is Irene, with three syllables. From the Greek . . . ei-re-ne . . . which means Peace.

But anyway, the point is, he has his chicken house down the bottom of the garden, with a sticking-out bit where you lift the lid to collect the eggs off the nests. If I stand on this egg-box I can just manage to stick one foot into a crack in the bricks and pull myself up onto the top of the garden wall, and drop down the other side where it isn't so high. That's the way I go over to play with Anna and her brother, or sometimes with May and Edna in the next-door house.

Their houses are just as big as ours. But only a father and mother and two children in each one! I've known that for ages, but I only just thought about it.

Ho hum! That must be not bad. Especially with your mother not being every-minute-of-the-day busy.

Not that my Mum wants to. She doesn't do it for fun, only to Make Ends Meet. I don't suppose they pay you much, to sing in opera.

To get back to the seven stairs. They bring you down to the landing window that looks out on the tucked-away bit of back garden inside the L-shape, and you can just see the flowering syringa bush and ferns in the rockery.

Next to the landing window, but up one step, is Devonshire Grannie's Room where Miss Fazackerly lives.

And up two different steps and along a side passage are, first the Bathroom, next the Upstairs Lavatory, and last of all - away in the dark - my Linen Cupboard.

8

DEVONSHIRE GRANNIE'S ROOM

A gentle wind stirs the curtains and wafts may tree scent in at the window. Or blows in crisp crimson leaves autumn-falling from the creeper on the sill.

Shafts of sun lean in and rest on silvery hair and quiet hands at work with needle and thread. Or light the straight back held steady in thoughts of peace.

There is hustle and bustle in the Kitchen below, and up and down the stairs, and all around. But here is quiet.

That was me trying to think like poetry about the past, when Devonshire Grannie was alive. But it is a quiet, calm room, even now.

If I had to choose any room in the house to be my own, this would be it. It has the same view as my mother-and-father's room, except it's one floor lower, so if you lean right out of the window you feel really close to the garden. Not that there's all that much special in the garden. Just the apple trees, the chicken house, the may trees and some hollyhocks, and the syringa bushes (that are supposed to be called mock-orange, and have a lovely scent, but we call them syringa) and my Dad's Madam Butterfly rose bush, and lots of grass to play on. Nobody has time to do things to the garden, not like next door with all the flowers.

But it's nice. And it makes the room gardeny.

Also the room is handy, because it's so close to the Bathroom and everything, and only one flight to go downstairs.

But it was my Devonshire Grannie who made the room calm. Do you suppose she still does?

Where did that thought come from? It's a strange thing to think. She died nearly three years ago when I was eight. But I still think of it as her room.

Anyway, she was my mother's mother and came from Devon to live with us after my Grandad died. She had a bad hip and used crutches, but she was tall and big-boned like my mother (and like me, too) and had a very straight back. She sat nearly all the time in the chair in her room, doing the mending, with her feet together and her knees together and her long skirt smoothed down over her lap, and her back and neck and head going up in a straight line, and very beautiful.

Her soft and silvery hair was piled up on top of her head, like Queen Mary. She wore creamy embroidered blouses with little standing-up boned collars, and her delicate gold and coral Cupid's-bow-and-arrow brooch.

She had a quiet smile, and dimples, like my mother, though she didn't laugh much, nor tell us stories. Sometimes she would read from the Devon Gazette. And also, I suppose, from the little book that she kept tucked down behind her cushions, called *In Tune With the Infinite*, which had beautiful thoughts in it, about God and eternity. But mostly she sat with her sewing things on a little table beside her and a big basket on the floor with all our clothes that needed mending, and stitched and patched and darned.

Apart from my mother, Devonshire Grannie was the most unlazy person I ever saw. Here are the things she did:

1. Darning all our socks, with a wooden mushroom and a big needle of wool.
2. Sewing patches and darning jerseys.
3. Making long-sleeved things into short-sleeved when

60

they went through at the elbow.
4. Sewing on school name tapes.
5. Turning cuffs that got frayed.
6. Turning collars. The part that turns over, and rubs on your neck, wears out first from being scrubbed. So if the shirt or blouse is still good you have to unpick the collar, turn it, and sew it on again. It's a really long job.
7. Darning linen tablecloths and the sheets with fine ' 'hite thread, or patching sheets if they're too far gone.
8. Crocheting for a change, her silver crochet hook going in and out, round the thread and back in, the patterns growing like magic.

I suppose you could say that I didn't know Devonshire Grannie very well, as she seldom said much. But she was good at listening. And sometimes people tell you a lot about themselves by *not* speaking.

My idea is, she was sorry my mother had to work so hard. So she helped as much as she could, not just by doing the mending but by Not Being a Trouble.

In a boarding-house, some people ring the bells in their rooms an awful lot. It makes a terrible jangling racket in the Kitchen. A black-and-white disc waggles to and fro frantically in a box up on the wall, to tell you which room it is.

Devonshire Grannie never rang bells. If she ever really needed anything she would knock twice on the floor with the rubber end of her crutches. If I was there in the Kitchen I would run up and ask her what she wanted. The door opened over the dark green linoleum with a soft shushing sound, because it had a felt roll fixed along the bottom to keep out the draughts.

One day I was in the Kitchen and there came a terrifying pounding of wild knocking from above, not like my Grannie's knock at all. I started for the door, an awful fear inside me.

But my mother was already running. She put out an arm and pushed me back, and cried in a strange voice, "*No!* Stay there!"

I was not allowed to go up.

The next day my brother and I were told that Jesus had taken Devonshire Grannie to heaven because he needed her, and we were shown her room so that we could see she wasn't there. We looked round the door, and my little brother cried out,

"Devonshire Grannie's forgotten her crutches!"

There was an awful silence, but then he said in a small, happy voice, "Oh, I forgot! She won't need them any more."

Even today it is a quiet, calm room and perhaps that is because of the one who lived in it. I had a word for her in my mind. I didn't know what it meant, nor where it came from, but it said: My Devonshire Grannie is a Wise-Woman.

So now Miss Fazackerly lives in the room, and I do think life is strange and people very contradictory. Because Miss Fazackerly is a Good Woman but I am not sure that she is wise.

Or maybe I'll discover that she is, but in a different way.

She is quite old, but her white hair is done up neatly on top, with no hair-nets or wispy bits like Miss Elphin. She always wears either her bright blue dress or her dark red dress, that comes down straight, almost to her ankles, with a silver chain and a cross that hangs upon her chest. She is a little bit short and stout and Queen Victoria-ish, but she moves briskly on her tiny tittuppy feet in black shoes with button straps. And she dusts her own room and comes down to breakfast, and is not a Bother.

The only time I go to her room is to take her hot-water bottle and her senna-pod tea at night. I make her senna-pod tea, too. It smells revolting. One teaspoonful of the broken-up bits out of her special little box. Put it in the tea-strainer on top of her cup, pour boiling water on it, wait sixty seconds, and hold your nose.

Also, Count-Your-Blessings. Because:

1. She is *not* a whingy moaner like Miss Elphin.
2. She is *not* bossy and selfish like Mrs W, which I'll tell about later.
3. She keeps herself to herself, is not noisy, takes brisk walks, and goes to church.

So you'd imagine that being a Good Woman would make her a nice person, but this is not necessarily so.

She has pernickety eyes that watch everything and everyone. Especially me, at Sunday dinner. And says, "I'd rather keep you

62

a week than a fortnight!" just because I like my Mum's meals and sometimes get a second helping.

And she looks down her nose and says, "In *my* young day we were taught to leave a little on our plates!"

Would you believe it! She actually does! Leaves a little bit pushed to one side to show she's not greedy. It is Good Manners, she says, but I think it's just A Shame, even though it's only a titchy bit. But an awful nuisance when you're stacking the plates for washing up.

What a silly Miss Fazackerly.

And yet . . .

Maybe her inside is different from her outside, like me.

Maybe she gets cross with herself because the two don't match up. Who knows? I don't!

So I'll wait and see.

And I'll tell you a thing. Here it is:

One day Miss Fazackerly was picking out some of her own books to take to a Sale of Work. She called me up to her room and said, "Now, I know you try to be a good girl and help your Mother, so you may choose one book for yourself if you wish."

Well!

I nearly took one about the moon and stars but it was a bit old-fashioned, and we already have a star map. So I chose one called *Apocrypha*. I don't know what that means. All it says inside is 'The APOCRYPHA according to the Authorised Version', and on the first page 'Hilda Fazackerly. Christmas, 1883', so she must have had it when she was quite young. I expect the tiny printing is too small for her eyes, now.

I liked it because it is so little, with a soft black leather cover, and that word in curly gold letters.

I said, "Thank you very much!" and took it to my room and flipped over the pages.

And look what I found, where Miss Fazackerly had put a line all down the margin:

But the angel of the Lord came down into the oven together
with Azarias and his fellows, and smote the flame of the fire out

of the oven;

And made the midst of the furnace as it had been a moist whistling wind, so that the fire touched them not at all, neither hurt nor troubled them.

Then the three, as out of one mouth, praised, glorified, and blessed God in the furnace, saying:

Blessed art thou, O Lord God of our fathers: and to be praised and exalted above all for ever . . .

Blessed art thou that beholdest the depths . . .

Isn't that fantastically *marvellous?* I like 'O Lord God of our fathers' and 'thou that beholdest the depths'. And it's pretty exciting about the oven.

It goes on and on, calling on all the most beautifully glorious things that ever were . . . angels, and sun and moon, the stars of heaven, winds, fire and heat, dews and storms of snow, lightnings and clouds . . . and whales and all that move in the waters, the fowls of the air, all beasts and cattle, and children of men, and:

O ye spirits and souls of the righteous, bless ye the Lord:
O ye holy and humble men of heart, bless ye the Lord:
praise and exalt him above all for ever.

Well!

I don't know *what* I feel.

Is Devonshire Grannie one of the spirits and souls of the righteous? And how about the holy and humble bit?

Ho hum!

It makes me think. About an awful lot of things.

And, Miss Fazackerly . . .

People are *very* mysterious.

9

THE LINEN CUPBOARD

Today is Paint-the-Bathroom-Lino Day. It only happens once a year, in the spring.

The Bathroom window is open and the curtains blowing, and my mother is crawling around on her hands and knees painting everything she can lay hands on.

Well, not quite. Not the walls. And not the inside of the bath. But a lot.

She starts in the far corner and works backwards, so as not to get marooned. She dips her brush into her tin of special green lino paint, and hums to herself, and I know she is thinking how nice to make everything as pretty and fresh as possible, now that the sun is shining.

The things she paints are:

1. The gas meter and all the pipes.
2. The stone sink place to catch the drips under the wash-basin.
3. The little wooden chair with the fretwork seat.

4. The sides of the bath, as far as she can reach, and its feet like lion's paws.
5. All the lino on the floor.

The pattern on the lino got worn off years ago, just where we walk, so doing this every year is like giving it a new green skin, to keep it going.

Besides, my Mum likes painting things. It's better than standing over a hot stove. She's good with a hammer and tacks, too - much, much better than my Dad - and re-does the webbing under the chair seats when they get saggy.

The reason I'm telling about the Bathroom first is that it, and the Upstairs Lavatory, have their doors on the long dark passage that leads to the Linen Cupboard where I sleep.

And all three of them are underneath the Tank Cupboard and the Room Next to the Tank Cupboard.

So all of them look out onto the brick wall which is the huge high side of the next-door house.

There are two interesting things in the Bathroom, and one is the geyser. There's no hot water in the taps, so when you want a bath you put pennies in the meter, then turn on the water and there is a colossally tremendously huge 'WHOOMPH!' as if the place is blowing up. But it's only the gas jets lighting up with a great sheet of flame.

Once the jets settle down, you can see them through the fancy openings round the bottom of the geyser, like fretwork done in copper. There must be fifty flames at least, arranged in circles like birthday-cake candles, and the water is hot very quickly with clouds of steam.

The old ladies have their baths run for them, usually by me, as they'd be scared out of their wits by the bang. I collect their pennies, put them in the meter and tell them when it's ready. The other boarders are on their honour to put pennies in. But if it's family we just pull out the metal box that the money drops into, take out about fivepence, and feed it back into the meter - clunk, clunk, clunk.

As it's pennies, we don't put a padlock on it, but the bedroom gas-fires have shilling-in-the-slot meters. That's one of my Saturday jobs, going round unpadlocking and taking the shillings down to the Kitchen table. I count them into piles of ten, so that two piles make £1, and my mother puts them away to help pay the gas bill.

People don't want a bath every day, but the guests like hot water, which is why we have this row of tall white enamel jugs that get filled up in the Kitchen and carried up to the wash-stands.

I'd hate to wash in hot water every day. It has such a staying-off-school-because-you're-ill-in-bed feeling. I just wash in cold at the wash-basin.

My father likes to wash at the bath. He hangs his old brown dressing-gown on the door, takes off his pyjama jacket and turns the cold tap of the bath on full, then sticks his head under the tap and splashes all over his chest, making happy noises like someone jumping into a freezing cold sea. He rubs his hair dry so hard, it goes into little curls all over, and he doesn't look like the same Dad at all, until he smooths it down again with a wet comb.

The other interesting thing is his box of Homeopathic Medicines, because they have names from plants, like Belladonna, Bryonia, Pulsatilla and Nux Vomica. They are little glass bottles with corks, full of tiny sugar-coated pills. His green booklet with 'Dr Durden's Notebook' on the cover, tells him what to give us for coughs and things. And if we have a really awful cold, he says in a deep witch's spell sort of voice, "Bed, Bath and Bryonia!"

The box doesn't have a lid. It just sits there on the window-sill. And now and then, maybe about once a week, I sneak one of the Bryonia. I don't *like* to say I do that, but I do. They have a fasci-nating bitter taste under the sugar. Well, it's 'three pilules three times a day before meals' or something like that, so one a week can't do much to me.

I don't like telling about the Upstairs Lavatory, either. But if I don't, you won't understand what it's like sleeping next door to it.

The Upstairs Lavatory is a long, narrow room with the WC on a little platform up the window end, and an old painted cistern high up on metal brackets, and a pull-chain with a white china handgrip.

Sometimes when you pull the chain the water starts rising up the pan and then I run for the door really fast, in case it overflows.

One day it really did overflow.

Oh, horrible and scarey!

Slow and silent the water inches higher and higher. You feel so helpless. There's no way you can stop water from flowing.

It came down onto the floor and over the edge of the platform and started following me to the door. There's a round thumb-catch you have to slide along, to open the door, and that day it stuck. I thought I'd never get it open.

For ages after that I didn't dare lock the door. Which was all right because you can hear people coming along the passage, and mostly they're pretty slow. But one day I heard light, quick steps coming fast. Almost in the same second the door was opening and Mr Sprigget was half-way in before I could stand up.

Poor Mr Sprigget! He must have had an awful shock! You could tell, by the way he sort of gulped, "Oops!" and backed out double-quick.

He never mentioned it. But I kept out of his way after that, just in case. Why does life have to be so embarrassing?

I am going down the long, dark passage to my door, the door of the Linen Cupboard. There is no window and no light. It's so dark, you can't see, only feel, and imagine spooky things coming at you.

I shut my eyes and put my arms out and charge along till I feel the door handle. Once I'm inside it's all right.

The Linen Cupboard is called that because all the wall between the door and the little window is cupboards, from floor to ceiling, with slatted shelves for sheets and towels and things. Once there were doors to the cupboards, but they have been taken off to make room for my bed. My bed fits tightly, with a wall on one side and the cupboards on the other.

To get to the window you have to walk along the top of the bed and off the end. There's just room for a small chair on the left of the door, beside my bed, for a book and my torch. And above the bed there is a little roundy-shaped mahogany shelf on a bracket, where I arrange my collection of dogs.

I've only got five so far, all about matchbox size - an Airedale, a Wire-haired Terrier like my Tigger, a Scottie, a West Highland and a Sealyham. I always stand the Wire-haired up with his paws on the Airedale's back, because he's lively and alert, as if he's being a look-out and seeing what's going on.

But every day when I come back from school my mother has put him down again.

They look so stiff and stodgy and uninteresting, all standing flat on their feet. So I put him up again. And she puts him down, but without saying why. If it's because he would fall down and break, she would say. Which means it's some grown-up reason that she's shy of mentioning.

Yesterday I managed to blurt out, "*Why* do you keep putting Tigger down?"

And she just said, "Darling, it's not *nice!*"

I couldn't ask her any more. For one thing, I wouldn't be able to shove the words out past my teeth - sometimes you just *can't*. But the main reason was because tears had started to come into her eyes, the way they do when she tries to explain about some things, like what will happen when I grow up a bit more. So that's that.

But *why* does it have to be so embarrassing?

And there's another thing.

Not so long ago, one night I got an orangey-coloured pencil and crayonned all my toe-nails to look like Esmé Hickman who comes to school with nail varnish. And I forgot I'd done it. My mother saw it in the morning when she came to hurry me up for breakfast, and said, "*What have you done?*" in an awful voice, as if I had done something terrible.

I was so frightened, I said, "Nothing! Nothing! I haven't done anything!"

So she said, "Well, if you haven't then you must be very ill and we'll have to send for the doctor!" and started taking my blouse off and trying to put me back to bed. So of course we had an awful time with my Mum crying, and me crying and howling and owning up, and going and scrubbing it off and being late for school.

Now, *why? Surely* my Mum could have seen it was only crayon? Or licked her finger and rubbed some off, and had a *laugh?*

Perhaps she was just doing what she thinks mothers are supposed to do. She doesn't like doing it, it's not her real self, and we hug and make up afterwards. It must be a Bother, having children being naughty, with all the boarders to look after as well.

Never mind! She doesn't usually go on like that. But then, I don't usually do anything wrong.

A thing that isn't too good about sleeping in the Linen Cupboard is water, and what it might do. There's the Upstairs Lavatory right next door to me, just through the wall, and the time the water came up and up the pan and followed me to the door.

And there's the water furiously fuming and hissing and bubbling in the Tank Cupboard just upstairs, and what would happen if it came over the top and through the ceiling.

But I can't hear any of that, when I'm in bed.

What I *can* hear, is this. Terrifying *drips!*

Whenever the overflow pipes are overflowing, either from the Tank Cupboard or from the cistern in the lavatory, they drip at night down the wall outside my window . . . drip, drip, drip, drip . . . and they are going into the side passage. It is narrow and high like a canyon, brick walls on either side. Or like a canal lock when it is empty and then the water rises up and up.

In the daytime I know that the drips won't do anything, just make a small puddle.

But at night when I'm asleep, I don't know that. And I do get nightmares about it. Not screaming nightmares. Just dream ones, of the passage filling right up with water till it comes up past my window and up and up and nothing can stop it.

But it's not something you can tell anyone about. They'd just say, "Don't be silly!"

And that makes sense.

The shelves are handy, though. It's nice having so much shelf just by the bed, inside the Linen Cupboard cupboards.

Last Easter I was given *six* Easter Eggs, the big hollow ones of dark chocolate that you can break bits off, like a chicken breaking out of its shell.

70

I kept them in a row on the wooden slats and when I'd been tucked up for sleep I got up again with my torch, and had a bit off each one every night in bed.

If my father is home in the evenings he'll sometimes come to the Linen Cupboard and sing to me. He stands just inside the door, with the door open to make room for his elbow because he's always more comfortable singing with one hand on his hip.

Sometimes it's *Old Simon the Cellarer*, which is a bit teasing-naughty of him, because it has a chorus that goes: 'What, marry old Marjorie? - No, no, no!' and my Aunt Marjorie is his sister and is fat and jolly and not married.

Sometimes it's *As I Walked Out One Morning from Tipperary Town*, which is about a young man falling in love with a colleen, but she keeps saying, "No!" until he tells her he has:

> ' . . . . got a cabin,
> and pigs that number seven,
> and och, with you mavourneen,
> sure, the place would be like heaven.'

and then her eyes look up into his, and the song just says:

> 'the little pigs had done it!
> Och, the dear little girl!'

and then I ask him, "Dad, what does 'the little pigs had done it' mean?"

Because I know what it means. And I know he knows that I know. So that is just *me* being teasing-naughty, to see if he'll answer. But he never does.

If he feels cross with me for asking he'll say, "Oh, put a sock in it!" or else just say, "Good night!" and shut the door and go away.

Other times he'll lift his eyebrows and look at me sideways, saying nothing, and finish up by singing his favourite, which is *I Must Go Down to the Seas Again, to the Lonely Sea and the Sky*. He has a very beautiful deep bass voice. Only it's not just the way he sings it, but how he looks when he sings it . . . not at me, but away somewhere else.

My Dad has never owned a boat, but he has always wished he did. He still sometimes reads *Swallows and Amazons* and *Coot Club* and anything he can get at the library with pictures and diagrams about small boats and how to sail them. And when he sings 'all I ask is a tall ship and a star to steer her by', and then the bit at the end that goes:

> '. . . and a grey mist on the sea's face,
> and a grey dawn brea . . . king.'

there's something there, in his voice, and in his face, that tells me what he's like inside.

But there aren't any words for it.

However, that song is really too high for him. He has one hand on his hip (I think that's to balance his hoppity leg) and cups the other hand behind his ear for the top notes, to hear the pitch.

The best song for him, and for me, and my absolute favourite, is *The Old Superb*. It's about a ship of Nelson's fleet that is just about fit for the scrap-yard, but it won't give up or let him down, and sails all night to catch up, 'round the world if need be, and round the world again, with a lame duck lagging, lagging all the way.'

It just sings itself, and my Dad's voice follows it and carries it and goes runningly and joyfully and then down . . . down . . . down deep till it shivers in your toes. And when he turns on full power for the chorus, with:

> 'Westward Ho! for Trinidad!
> And Eastward Ho! for Spain!
> And Ship Ahoy! a hundred times a day . . . '

I can imagine all the house full of boarders standing at their doors with their ears flapping and their hearts full of happiness.

I don't know if they do, mind you. But that's the way I feel. It just *blows* away brick walls and drips and spooky passageways, and makes the Linen Cupboard into a place I wouldn't in a million years swap for anywhere else.

All that is true. But there's more to the song than that.

If I'm to be truthful, I have to say that the reason it's my favourite is to do with things that there aren't any words for. If I

72

write down the verse, I suppose it'll sound like nothing special. But it is.

It's about the lame duck's courage, and about keeping going and never giving up . . . and Nelson knowing but not telling . . . and the way my Dad sings the last three lines.

> 'The Old Superb was barnacled and green as grass below,
> Her sticks were only fit for stirring grog.
> The pride of all her midshipmen was silent long ago,
> And long ago they ceased to heave the log.
> Yet all day long and all night long
> Behind the Fleet she crept,
> And how she fretted none but Nelson guessed . . . '

It's as if he's singing about himself.

And me too, perhaps.

And then that chorus that brings the house down, all glorious and joyful.

Ho hum! Time to sleep.

d

10

SOMETIMES A THING IS A PERSON

When you run down the fourteen stairs from Miss Fazackerly's
and the Bathroom and all that, you get to the Front Hall, and this
is what you see.

On your right are three things.

First, an elegant narrow arch which is the start of another dark
passage leading to the Downstairs Lavatory. You can see my
father's old fawn mackintosh and ancient grey hat hanging up on
the first of a row of hooks. If you go down the passage, there are
other coats and hats and my satchel and things brushing against
you in a friendly way, so the dark doesn't matter.

Next is the door of the Lounge, which is in the front of the
house with the Blue Room up above it. This door, and the outsides of all the doors in the house, as well as the skirting-boards
and stair treads, are chocolate-brown paint. My mother would
never have chosen it, for she loves springtime colours. So it must
have been like that when they came, when I was born, and once
you've got chocolate-brown paint, it goes on and on for ever.

The third thing is the hall chair and table and umbrella stand,

and then you're at the front door. And on the opposite side of the hall is the Downstairs Bedroom (which is in the front of the house with Mr Grüning's up above it) and then the Dining Room.

The hall chair is very important, because you have to sit down on it to get your mouth opposite the telephone mouthpiece, which is like a black daffodil. I answer the phone and run and get whoever it's for, and my mother uses it to order coal and groceries. If the guests make a call they put the right money in the black tin box with red and gold lines and a brass handle.

The other thing on the hall table, apart from the telephone directories and message pad, is the Dinner Gong. If I happen to be in the Kitchen at the right moment, I can run along the Kitchen passage and up the three steps and along the Front hall and ring the gong to tell the guests that dinner is ready.

You pick it up by the brass bit at the top, hold it so that it hangs free, and hit it with the furry drum-stick. Not too hard, not too soft, and about twice as fast as a clock striking . . . bong-bong-bong-bong-bong-bong-BONG!

So I suppose you could say that one of the things you'd see in the Front Hall, is *me!*

Except when I'm at school, or in the Kitchen, or out in the garden, or in the Dining Room in the evenings doing painting or homework, I seem to be in the Front Hall quite a lot, one way or another.

If you were a boarder you'd see me there quite often, but I don't expect you would *notice* me. Not that I'm titchy or mousey. No, I'm just tall-for-my-age and ordinary-ish, in a cotton frock, or an old skirt and jersey and socks, and my not-very-wavy short brown hair parted on one side and looped up in a kirby-grip on the other. And you'd be so used to seeing me whizzing around in my tom-boy sort of way, whistling or humming, and shoving a mop around the hall lino, or bringing the big tray to set the table for dinner, and putting it down on the dumb-waiter thing while I open the door, that you wouldn't look twice.

After all, I'm just a *child*. I know that! And very soon you'd run out of things to say. You can't keep on year after year saying, "There's a good girl!" and "What a lovely day!"

That's one reason why it's a good idea for me to do the running backwards and forwards. If it was my mother, she'd never get her work done. The stew would stick, or the cakes would burn, or the jam boil over. Because it would be:

"Oh, have you a minute to see to . . . "

or:

"Oh, you're so clever with your needle, could you possibly ..."

or:

"I think my hot-water bottle may be leaking . . . "

or:

"What a delicious pudding that was last night! Would you have a minute to write out the recipe for my niece?"

And *that* is more than enough of *that!*

No, if you were a boarder, and I was working around about, the only time you *might* notice me is if I was dusting the stairs and you wanted to get past. That's one of my jobs and you wouldn't believe how much dust arrives on the treads every day. I have to start at the top of the house and work down, crawling backwards, brushing the carpet runner, re-fixing the rods that have kicked loose, and dusting the sides and the banisters.

I hate to say it, but if you were in the front hall, the back view of me coming down, raising a small cloud of dust, and humming *Fight the Good Fight* or something like that, would certainly be noticeable.

I just hope you wouldn't see my navy-blue school knickers, which is the only sort I've got.

It's about time I told about the Downstairs Bedroom.

A boarding-house is a strange sort of place. Some people stay with us for years, like Wrightie, and Mr Grüning. But when they come and go, it's a bit like the kaleidoscope that Granpie made me, the patterns keep shifting and the colours change.

You can't remember all about people, when they've been gone for years, or even months. Only the thing that sticks in your mind.

For instance, one of the Downstairs Bedroom families, a long while back, had a girl a little bit older than me, called Lesley Mercy Proctor. She used to take us round to her school-friend's garden shed where a gang of them used to play at hospitals, with garden syringes for pretend-injections, and bottle-tops pressed onto your arm to make vaccination marks.

It wasn't much fun being a patient, and not my idea of an interesting game, either. I'd rather dig tunnels in the garden with my brother, or go train spotting with Granpie.

But I always liked her name. It's the sort of name you can say over to yourself - Lesley Mercy Proctor.

One day, there was a Miss Gibb supposed to be coming to live in that room. She was dark-haired and as tall and thin as a lamp-post and I've a feeling she was a very nice person, but we'd no chance to find out.

You will hardly believe this, but it's true. When she arrived she had about seven fox terriers on leads, and took them into the bedroom with her - in a boarding-house! They were all in there with the door shut, all barking and yipping and yapping at once, and the whole place was in an uproar.

The next day the poor dogs were still yipping and yapping and barking and howling and yowling non-stop, but they were doing it down the bottom of the garden in the chicken house, which happened not to have chickens in it at the time.

And the next day they were gone, and Miss Gibb too. And my mother on her hands and knees scrubbing the bedroom floor.

When you're a child, you know what you can see with your eyes and hear with your ears, but you don't get told the reasons for why things happen.

Sometimes you get a clue, however.

In the Downstairs Bedroom now, is Mrs W, who is so incredibly dreadful and bossy that she doesn't deserve to have anything nice said about her. But . . . she's been here about six months, and her Bank Manager son and his wife, who are pretty old themselves, come and visit her . . . and my mother said it's obvious they don't want her at home, so they've sent her to us.

It must be awful to be Not Wanted, and we try to be sorry for her. We *try!* But . . .

You know what Mr Toad is like in *Wind in the Willows*. He's rich and proud, and when he has to be disguised so as to escape from jail, he is affronted to be dressed as a washerwoman . . .

Well, that's what Mrs W is - rich and proud, and affronted to be in a boarding-house. Also - and I am not making this up - if you think of the fat, squashy toad figure, and the flabby big-mouthed, squinched-sideways Mr Toad face, and dress it in expensive but old-fashioned lacy black clothes with lots of long black petticoats and a lacy black cap, and make the Mr Toad face bright red with a broad purple nose - that, I am very sorry to say, really and truly *is* Mrs W.

It is hard to understand what she is like, or why.

It is hard to believe what she did one day at Sunday dinner.

There we all were, being pleasant to one another, and lovely smells of roast potatoes and gravy and vegetables wafting over from the sideboard where my mother was carving the big roast leg of lamb. And there was Mrs W, not conversing, just waiting, like a big fat baby with her napkin tucked under all her chins and her back propped up on two pillows.

When her plate was put in front of her, and the serving dishes of sprouts and carrots offered, she started banging her knife and fork up and down and going purple all over her face, shouting, "*All* I want is *one egg!* Lightly *boiled!* And a thin slice of *toast!* - gobble - gobble - gobble - Do you *hear* me? - gobble - gobble - Egg and *toast!*"

And my mother had to go and get it.

Ho hum! What can you do?

We are all afraid that one day she really will blow up.

In between the Downstairs Bedroom and the Dining Room is a little bit of wall that is useful for three things. These are:

1. The Hall Clock, which is like a small Grandfather Clock hanging on the wall. It chimes and strikes the hours and you can see the big pendulum going to and fro so solemnly through the glass, and hear the slow, chunky sound of the 'Tick . . . Tock, Tick . . . Tock!' Winding and setting the clocks is my father's job.
2. The Dumb-Waiter Thing, which is for resting trays on, and is a sort of folding trestle with webbing straps across the top.
3. The big black shiny tin Oil Stove, with an openwork pattern on top to let the warmth out, and it's very handy in the winter. There's a brass knob for turning the wick up or down, and you can see the flame

through a little mica window at the bottom.

Of course, one of the main things about the Front Hall is the three steps you have to go down, before you even begin going along towards the Kitchen. You have to be careful not to catch your heel, because however many times the lino on the steps is mended, it wears out again pretty quickly.

I bet whoever thought up those steps, never tried carrying hundreds of trays of roasts, vegetables, toad-in-the-holes, gravy boats, apple-pie-and-custards, steamed treacle puddings and sherry trifles *up* them, nor hundreds of trays back *down* them again, stacked with all the dishes, bowls, glasses, cutlery, side plates and greasy dinner plates for the washing-up.

Whoever invented those three steps, ought to have invented a flying trolley.

Another thing you might come across in the Front Hall, isn't a *thing* . . . it's Granpie.

He's really, really good at mending and fixing things, in fact it's what he likes doing best.

Granpie is quite old, and a little bit bent because of taking me out in a push-chair when I was little, and bending over to talk to me and tell me about the interesting things we were seeing. He always wears his old grey suit with a waistcoat and an old-fashioned striped flannel shirt with a separate shiny white collar.

His suit is comfortably saggy from having so many useful things in the pockets, like a screwdriver and pliers, string and wire and penknife, a bag of sweeties and an extra hankie. And his trouser knees are a bit baggy from getting down to things.

Granpie lives in Acton with Acton Grannie, who is blind and doesn't leave the house. He comes over quite often, and if he spots something that needs tightening up or screwing down, or a touch of glue, or new wire or cord, like:
door handles
window sashes
chair rungs
draught strips
door locks and catches
then out come his tools and he won't notice anything else till the

job is done.

And all that the boarders might notice is a bent grey back, and a happy sound like a little bird twittering, which is Granpie whistling *Guide-Me-O-Thou*, very softly under his breath, to the tune *Cwm Rhondda*.

11

THE LOUNGE

Here is a room with a high white decorated ceiling and an old rosy-pink carpet. It has a big bow window, two wide panes with a narrow one each side, all of them very tall, reaching right up to the ceiling. The curtains are heavy purple cotton with elegant wide gold lines and narrow fawn lines down them. The old grey couch and armchairs have dark blue velvety seat-cushions with the same handsome gold and fawn lines from the back to the front edge.

And here is a memory from when I was little.

Three old ladies sit on the dark blue velvety cushions.

One lady is brisk and busy and sits well forward, peering through her gold-rimmed spectacles and writing on the little table in front of her, making spidery scribbles in one of her blue exercise books.

That is Miss Mole, and she has a purple jersey and skirt, and fawny-grey hair tied back in a bun.

But the other two ladies are all in black. One is Miss Abbot with her long, pale, flat face and her secret thoughts. And one is

Miss Doughty who is stout-bodied and stout-hearted, with a ready word of cheer. They prop their black button-strapped feet on little stools and knit grey wool socks, or chat, or fiddle with their fringy black shawls and dangling jet beads.

Sometimes they get up stiffly and slowly to ring the bell for more coal. Or if there's plenty they open the coal scuttle lid, lift the tongs off the brush-and-tong stand, and put another lump on the fire that is always burning.

While they are up out of the chair, they maybe look in the big mirror that goes all the way along the back of the black wood mantelpiece, and pat their hair, or take out a hair-pin and refix a wispy bit.

On the mantelpiece is a clock, and two bronzy-coloured candlesticks with tulip tops and swans at the side, with their necks stretching up. Just under the shelf of the mantelpiece are five little alcoves of black wood, with one precious and treasurey thing in each . . . two tiny turquoise pots with tall, thin necks . . . two mother-of-pearl shells that spiral round and round to pointy tops, and have scratched pictures of scrolls and mermaids and ...

One great big ancient shell that sits in the centre of the others, snail-shell shaped, with greeny bits and shiny bits and pinky-pearly bits, that you can really and truly hear the sea in, like surf roaring on coral strands far away.

The Lounge is still exactly like that. Nothing has changed, not one little thing. Except that now, the clock only goes if one side is propped up on a matchbox. And the rosy-pink carpet had to be moved round last year, to hide the worn bits.

But the three old ladies have gone.

After them came Wrightie who was my friend, and other people who come and go, and Mr Grüning who sits there just sometimes, to spread out *The Times* on the big round table by the window, or to join the ladies for Afternoon Tea.

Mr Sprigget and Mr Ashley go to work, and after dinner in the evening they go out, or to their rooms, and don't bother much with the Lounge.

So now it is Miss Fazackerly, usually in her blue dress with the silver cross, on one side of the fire where Miss Mole used to sit. And Miss Elphin in fawn, on the couch at the other side. And

Mrs W in all her black things, propped and bolstered up in the chair opposite the fire.

I can't tell much about what they say to each other, because I'm only in and out of the room to answer the bell if they ring for more coal or a glass of water. But Mrs W seems to be the only one who says a lot. It always sounds like the tail end of something to make the others feel unhappy, like showing off about being the only one who's been married and having a son in a good position in the Bank.

Or sometimes I think she's been telling Miss Fazackerly that she is wrong to waste her time writing letters to other people. Or telling Miss Elphin what a dreadful shade of pink she is using to knit a cardigan for her niece, which is probably true but no need to say it.

Miss Elphin answers in a moany voice that it's Myrtle's favourite colour.

Miss Fazackerly gives her usual sort of polite but sarcastic snort down her nose, or maybe gives a sharp answer under her breath, like saying, "*Some* people have been well brought up!"

Mrs W, instead of wearing little black indoor shoes with a strap across the instep, wears something you'll think I am imagining, but I'm not. I've had to lace them up for her too often to be imagining it - long boots of very soft black leather that come half-way up her legs and are tied tight with laces that go round little knobs, then criss-cross, then round the next knobs, criss-cross again and so on up to the top, wind the laces round the top of the boot to use up the spare, and finish with a bow.

And maybe undo it and start all over again, if it's too tight or too loose.

Unless it's holidays, it's a Saturday morning job. She'll shout, "Someone do my boots! Fetch that *child!*" and I have to get down on my knees and take her foot in my lap.

I think maybe sometimes my brother has done it for her, even though he is only little. Anyway, one Saturday she gave us a whole half-crown each. I have to admit - that was generous. A lot more than my sixpence a week pocket-money and thruppence-more-if-I don't-bite-my-nails.

But - was I allowed to put it in my money-box to save up for something really good? No! I was to go to W.H. Smith's and I was to go *now* and come back and show her what I'd bought.

That's what Mrs W said. And I had to.

So I went to Smith's, but I already had plenty of crayons and paper and pencils and my birthday fountain pen. And it wasn't enough to buy the sort of books I like, that I get for Christmas. The only thing left to choose was an Annual and I chose a Billy Bunter one,which I'd never had before. I quite looked forward to it.

And she wouldn't let me keep it.

I argued and explained but she started going pop-eyed and red and unreasonable, as she always does unless she has her own way, shouting, "Go and take it back, take it back *immediately* - gobble - gobble - the very idea! Tell them I said you were to change it - gobble - gobble - and buy a pencil case instead! A *pencil* case, do you hear me? *A pencil case!*"

So I did. Straight away.

The only sort you could buy for half-a-crown were nasty leatherette ones with little loops for putting pencils in and a zip all round. And I already have my lovely wooden one with the slide lid and swing-out section. Still, it's red, so it's not too bad and I expect it will be useful.

And I ought to feel grateful.

Only I'm *not!*

Because I wanted to *choose*, not be told.

I was just thinking. What is it that makes people happy? I mean, *really* happy. You can tell by their faces.

My mother is happy when I come into the Kitchen, and my brother too. She turns round from the stove, and however tired she was looking her face goes smiley and comfortable, and she says, "Come and help me and we'll do it together!"

Granpie enjoys things we do together, like going to look at the horses in the Council's stables, or sailing boats on the pond, or melting glue in the glue-pot. But you can tell by his face that's not the same, because he's being careful all the time, and watching that I don't get run over, or burned or something. But when he is mending and fixing things - that's when he's really happy.

My father is happy nearly all the time, I think. Or else he's sort of sad, but being sad and being happy are both somehow the same, for him. He doesn't have Worries, and he's peaceful -

except when we pester him and he has to tell us to go and boil our heads.

And I'm happy when I'm reading, or colouring pictures with my paint-box, or doing sums, or digging with the trowel in my bit of the garden which is all round the bottom of the right-hand may tree. In fact, I'm happy when I'm doing anything that I like doing, as long as it's all by myself, with no one Bothering me. So perhaps I'm selfish. Only everyone else has to be happy too, and peaceful, otherwise it's no good.

So how about our three old ladies?

Well, it's easy to find grumbly things to say about Miss Elphin and Miss Fazackerly, but they're really quite lovable in their own way. I mean, they're good-hearted and *want* to be kind, and have at least one thing each that makes them happy.

Mrs W, however, is only happy when she is having her own way, but that's not really happiness. Because having her own way isn't good for her or for us, and her face doesn't go peaceful, only gleeful-wicked.

So what does that make her?

And what made her like that?

Maybe someone knows, but I don't, she is just too complicated for me.

So I'll go back to the other two ladies, and do a bit more thinking. Because I'm not done with it yet by a long chalk, and if anyone isn't interested perhaps they wouldn't mind skipping over this bit while I finish working out about happiness.

All right.

Miss Elphin.

Miss Elphin is easy. She is mostly a miserable old soul and makes even a sunny day feel sodden, and takes up all the couch in the Lounge with her knitting bag and patterns, her extra fawn cardigan and bits of this and bits of that, and maybe props her legs up on it too. Nothing is ever just right for her, the room is too hot or too cold, the tea is too strong or too weak. She is anxious in case she gets a draught in her shoulders, or in case we fall down and break our legs. And if she reads anything out from *The Daily Telegraph*, she always picks on a disaster. She is a worrier.

But . . . once a week, every Wednesday evening, her niece

Myrtle comes. Myrtle sits on the couch with her and all Miss Elphin's worriedness goes away like snow in summer.

Myrtle Elphin is a dress designer, I think, or a fashion artist or something. Anyway, she always brings her big sketchbook to show her aunt. They sit side by side and spread it open on their knees and turn over the pages, while Myrtle explains about all the scratchy-looking drawings, the ladies with very long legs and sketched-in dresses and coats and hats and handbags.

Miss Elphin exclaims with pleasure, and asks questions, and her face is peaceful and quiet. She is happy.

She's happy all the while till Myrtle stands up to go away, and then the worried frown between her eyes comes back. She doesn't get up, but reaches up and stays holding onto her niece's hand as long as she can, and then lets go and always says exactly the same words, in her usual mournful, weepy, no-hope voice, "Take care of yourself, Myrtle, there aren't many of us left!"

Miss Elphin says this just as her niece is opening the Lounge door, so we can't help hearing. It starts sounding funny if you hear it for years, every week the same. I'm afraid we have a laugh about it, and it's turned into one of our sayings, "Take care of yourself, there aren't many of us left!"

But it *is* nice that Miss Elphin is happy, just once a week, and you can see why she says it. Because Myrtle is her family.

Miss Fazackerly . . .

Well, Miss Fazackerly is more difficult.

To try and work out what makes her happy, I have to talk about her a bit first. She is quite a cheering sight, being so brisk and active for her age, and her hair so snowy white, and wearing her nice dark red dress whenever the blue one goes to the cleaners. I don't think she's interested in clothes, but keeps herself neat and clean and wholesome and healthy because that's the way she was brought up.

She has a Good Brain and is impatient of foolish people who make ignorant remarks, or who are slack and sloppy and get themselves and their persons into a muddle.

Her eyes that are so quick to pick on faults, are also quick to notice if my mother has a headache, or if we've fallen and hurt ourselves. If help was needed, she'd help, but not fuss.

86

She is very strict with herself. And very church-religious and Sticks to her Principles, no matter what. For instance, she insists on going to Early Service on Sundays fasting, and refuses even a cup of tea, which makes my gentle mother worried and cross, in case she faints. Because she did, once, and got sent back in a taxi.

And once she rang the Dining Room bell and had me take away the marmalade off her breakfast tray because it was self-denial for Lent. Which seemed to me terribly funny but also a dreadful show-off, because she could just have left it.

But . . . my goodness, thinking about people is like that wooden doll I had once for Christmas, that the more you open it the more little wooden dolls there are inside . . . it *can't* have been show-off!

Because Miss Fazackerly really *is* strict and no-nonsense with herself.

The thing that's annoying about Miss Fazackerly is that she wants to do you good and put you right. She feels it's her *duty*.

So that is the clue.

She must have worked it out like this: If she just left the marmalade untouched I wouldn't have known it was a special time like Lent, and she wouldn't have been setting me a Good Example. Or rather, she would, but I wouldn't have known about it.

Whereas if she asked for the marmalade to be taken away, that would be Good-For-Me. *And*, if I thought she was being show-off, then that would be Good-For-Her, because it would be humbling to be thought ill of when she was doing it for Good Motives.

But then . . .

No! I don't *want* to be a detective about people. It's too complicated.

But, this business of happiness. It doesn't make Miss Fazackerly happy to put people right. You can tell by her face. She feels responsible, and does it as a duty, which is annoying but you can forgive her. So what makes her happy, if anything?

Perhaps I shouldn't say this, but when I take her senna-pod tea at 8 o'clock every evening, if I go in too quickly after knocking on the door she is often just getting up off her knees at the side of the big armchair where Devonshire Grannie used to sit, and she has her prayer book open on the arm of the chair. As she comes across to take the cup, and thank me, you can tell that she's happy. Her face is quiet and peaceful, and her eyes are not picking holes in me but looking at somewhere much nicer.

So that's my mother and father and Granpie and me and the old ladies, and that's enough . . . I think I've got it worked out now. Like doing factors and Least Common Denominators.

Here it is:

'Being happy is something that just comes - but it
only comes when people can forget about Worries
and Duties and Bothers.'

Now I can get back to the Lounge.

In winter, at holidays or weekends, when the afternoon begins to get dark I'm sometimes sent into the lounge to switch on the light and close the curtains, rattling the wooden rings along the rails, then get the round table ready for Afternoon Tea.

It's a beautiful table of polished golden wood, with only one leg in the middle that spreads out into four curly feet, and four chairs with heart-shaped backs and soft leather seats. I bring a tray from the Kitchen with four tea-time plates and cups and saucers, the tiny little bone-handled knives and matching tea-spoons, the rolled-up napkins and the tablecloth with embroidery corners, then put the tray on a chair-seat while I spread the cloth and set the table.

My mother comes along from the Kitchen with a plate of very thin bread-and-butter, or perhaps currant bread, or maybe freshly made scones, and the jam dish, and sometimes one of her fluffy sponge cakes. The old ladies leave their fireside chairs and sit up to table, and quite often Mr Grüning comes down from his room to join them. When they leave their armchairs and sit up, they seem to become more well-behaved, and are polite and kind to one another.

We come in again, me with the tall silver hot water-jug, and my mother carrying the silver tray with the silver Queen Anne teapot, milk jug and sugar bowl. Miss Fazackerly pours the tea and Mr Grüning hands it round and makes conversation with the ladies, while they take sugar lumps daintily with the sugar tongs, and stir, holding the teaspoons delicately with finger and thumb.

That is Afternoon Tea.

And the Lounge is like a different place altogether, with the soft light and the chink of china, and everyone on best behaviour like nursery tea in a story.

And here is another time, and the Lounge is like a fairy-tale, criss-crossed with paper-chains, and holly behind all the pictures.

We're all there, all the guests and all the family, in our best clothes, my Dad in his brown plus-fours, and my mother in the beautiful dark-blue, gold-rose-patterned voile that she's had for ever and ever, and me in my party dress of chestnut-coloured, gold-smocked velvet that my Mum made.

The fire is roaring up, with a log on top of the coals, the flames flicker and dance, and reflections shimmer and shine. My Dad sticks his pipe in the corner of his mouth, gets up and goes over to the door and switches off the light. The room comes alive with magic shadows, conversation sinks to whispers, and in the bright fire-glow he crosses to the corner by the window, strikes a match, and lights candle after candle on the big Christmas-tree.

One by one the little white stars come out, and wink and shine in among the pine needles on coloured balls and silver frost-hangings. The guests exclaim at the beauty and say, "Ooh!" and, "Ah!" and, "How lovely it all is!" and admire the star on the top, and the tiny turquoise or pink birds hiding their spun-glass tails among the branches.

And then we all go quiet again.

It's Christmas Day. We've all sung carols, and had Christmas Dinner with turkey and stuffing and Christmas pudding with holly on top and brandy flames licking all around the dish, and crackers and mottoes, trinkets and paper hats. We've had Christmas cake for tea, and all the work is finished.

And now we're waiting.

There's just the glow, and the white candles, the wonderful pine-needle scent filling the room, and people sitting, or perched on stools and chair-arms, and fire-lit faces waiting and listening . . . listening towards the door . . .

Then we hear it . . . a distant, slow, heavy tread of purposeful feet . . . and then the beginnings of a voice, coming nearer . . . or could it perhaps just be the wind, outside there in the night? . . . a strange sound, coming across Arctic wastes? . . .

For a moment we almost get magicked, we almost think it could really . . .

And then we all look at each other happily, and give a little laugh. Here comes the voice properly, singing something in slow, measured tones keeping pace with the feet, nearer and nearer all the time, until we can hear the words through the door:

> "Trudging through the ice and snow,
> Far away from the firelight's glow,
> I'm come from the land of frost and cold,
> Bearing gifts for young and old."

And the door bursts open and there he is! And we all say, "*Father Christmas!*"

Of course we know it's Granpie, wearing the costume he uses when he is Father Christmas for the children's party at Bethnal Green, but he's a jolly good one, and it's nice to pretend.

Also, he has a real sack full of real presents, and when he has trudged round the room in the fire-and-candle-light a few more times, singing a few more verses of his song that he's made up himself, we switch the light on and he stands by the tree and makes a great big happy thing out of reaching into his sack and taking out the little parcels in their Christmas wrapping paper, one at a time, and saying, "Who can this be for, do you suppose?" or, "Hallo! This says 'To Miss Elphin, from Santa Claus'."

They're all little things. Hankies, bath salts, special soap, home-made needle-books and pin-cushions, tobacco pouches and pipe cleaners, pretty note-paper and calendars. But everyone gets presents, things 'from Father Christmas', or from each other, or things we've made at school. And as well as our morning stockings with the orange in the toe, sugar mice and sweeties, a toy or a jig-saw or a game, my brother and I get one good present out of the mysterious sack.

I like waiting to see what my special present will be. Will it be something amazing, like my grown-up Windsor and Newton paintbox? Or will it be a book, a proper book with a long story I've never read before, and little black-and-white illustrations that

90

I can colour? It's a lovely thing to look forward to, and look at the wrapping, and feel it, and not know what it is till I've rustled the paper off.

But then, I like everything about the Lounge at Christmas-time, with everyone happy, and seeing the faces in the firelight.

It's the only time we really all feel like one family, even though we're not. And you sort of forget that they're old. Maybe Christmas makes them young again.

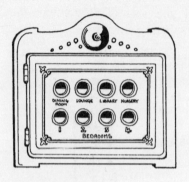

12

SOMETIMES THERE ARE
JUST TOO MANY PEOPLE

The Kitchen is the best place in the house.

When I get back from school, I come down the side passage and in through the Scullery, open the door to the Kitchen, and there it is. Home! A place where there's always something doing, not just people sitting around. And fresh air and nice cooking smells, not all stuffy.

The Kitchen is light, with white-washed walls and white paint. And it has a grand window that's low enough to climb in and out of to the garden, instead of going the long way round. In good weather the bottom of the window is nearly always wide open to let out the heat of the cooking, so even if you're busy you can smell the freshness and see the grass and trees. And in summer there's a sunflower patch and a nasturtium patch right opposite the window, that come up every year by themselves without anyone bothering about them.

And . . . the Kitchen is a place that belongs to *us*, to family, not boarders. I don't have to mind my manners or keep very quiet. I can come home and cut a thick slice of bread and put butter and golden syrup on it, and sit and eat it and read a book at the same time, and prop my elbows on the nice bare boards of the kitchen table. And while I cut the bread, or wash my plate up afterwards, I can whistle. I can whistle as much as I like!

We had a very ladylike kitchen helper once called Mrs Waitrose. She had a tight face and permed-up hair and a white coat like a dentist. If my mother wasn't around she used to act as though she was our governess or something.

"A whistling woman, a crowing hen,
    Is neither fit for God nor men,"

she used to recite at me in a prim and proper voice, with never a smile, and order me to stop.

That was a terrible thing to do! Fancy telling me what to do in my own home! We've always been a whistling family - and why not, I'd like to know? It's a good job she didn't stay long.

When I was little there was a big, dark, moustachey sort of helper called Ellen who came on Tuesdays and Thursdays. If I fiddled with left-over pastry bits at the table while she was making a pie, or nibbled the peelings as she pared them off the cooking apples, there'd come a cross sort of growly noise over my head. I'd look up with a start, being miles away, dreaming, and see her scowly black eyebrows and huge pink arms like giant uncooked sausages. She'd shake her fists, and roar, "*Get out of my Kitchen!*"

That was an awful feeling. I wasn't frightened. Just *banished!* Where had home gone to?

The only comfortable place left to go, was the garden. I'd run off down the bottom where no one could get at me, and look for Daddy-long-legses in the grass, or collect nasturtium seeds, or turn over old bits of wood and watch the slaters scurry away or roll up into tight balls like little armadillos.

But that is a long time ago.

For years now it has just been my mother, or on some days, my mother and Kitty Carter. Kitty is Welsh, and lovely, the nicest possible sort of person, with dark curly hair and rosy cheeks, and always having a hum or a sing to herself, and a smile for me, and happy always.

At the beginning Kitty even used to help me make things 'for the fairies' with the left-over pastry. She'd get out two patty-tins and we'd make little pies and put them out on the back step and they'd be gone in the morning. So she has grown up with us and is like one of the family.

With Kitty around, or when it's just my Mum, the Kitchen is busy and happy and comfortable. Our own place.

So I'll tell a bit about it.

When I sit at the kitchen table to do jobs, like slicing the runner beans, or grating suet or cheese, I sit with my back to the window so as to see the whole room and what's going on. The easiest way to explain the Kitchen is to pretend I'm sitting at the table like that, and go all the way round it starting from my left.

There are only two things on the left-hand wall. The first is an enormously huge giant-sized dresser, built onto the wall, and painted green. It has the usual shelves at the top, where we keep the biggest dishes for roasts and turkeys, and the china vegetable dishes with lids and handles. It has three big drawers, one for cutlery, one for tablecloths, tray cloths and cork mats, and the last one for useful odds and ends like candles and night-lights, hammer and tacks and pincers, paper bags that we smooth out and save, and string that we take off parcels and undo all the knots and roll up again to use. And it has an underneath place, with no cupboard doors, where we put the big tea-chest that comes once a year. You prise the plywood top off, tear back the tinfoil, and there's the whole box full of tea, ready to fill up the tea caddy whenever it's empty.

The second thing is the door to the Washing-Up Pantry. This is a little room, about the size of my Linen Cupboard, that runs the whole length of the wall, in behind the dresser. It has ancient wooden shelves stacked solid with all the rest of the china and glass, hooks for cups and mugs, and the row of enamel hot water-jugs on the floor below. Up the far end is a little window that looks out onto my Dad's Madam Butterfly rose bush. And beneath the window is the huge, deep, stone sink and old wooden draining-boards that get really soggy underneath where the water runs back. The only modern thing is the electric hot-water heater on the wall.

The Washing-Up Pantry also has something else.

Or rather, someone.

And that's Rose Walford.

I know I said there was just Kitty Carter. That's the way I *feel* about it. The others are sort of extras, two hours here and there, like Nellie-cleaning-the-steps that Mr Sprigget did the drawing of.

Rose Walford comes sometimes to do the mid-day washing-up. (I do it on Sundays.) She also does three other things, which are:

1. Telling me about her boy, and the time he tipped a kettle of boiling water over his arm and she saved him by emptying the golden syrup tin all down the scalded place to keep the blisters down, and how the doctor said this was a Very Good Thing.
2. Singing me sort of naughty songs, only I don't know why, because she leaves the naughty bits out and goes "hm - hm - hm" instead, and they're not very good anyway.
3. Rolling fag-ends in greaseproof paper and lighting them from the pilot light at the gas stove, and then rolling one for me, and making me try. But I can't make it work, and I don't like the taste, anyway.

And that's the end of the left-hand wall.

So we've come to the wall that's facing me as I sit at the kitchen table. Here there are four things.

On the left is the door into the house, that leads to the Cupboard Under the Stairs and up the three steps. The next thing on the wall is the Flap Table, which is a green-painted flap made of boards, that hangs down against the wall out of the way. When you need it, you lift it up, pull out the wooden brackets and . . . there's a handy place to put the tray, to stack it with hot food from the oven or cold dishes from the Pantry, before carrying it along to the Dining Room.

On the wall above the Flap Table, is the Bell Box, which is about the size of my school satchel, with glass in front like a picture frame. Behind the glass is a white board with eight holes, four in the top row and four in the bottom. Behind each hole is a black-and-white striped disc that waggles madly to and fro when its bell rings, and you look up quickly to see which room wants you. Each hole has a name printed under it, like this:

Dining Room	Lounge	Library	Nursery
Bedroom 1	Bedroom 2	Bedroom 3	Bedroom 4

We don't have a Library or a Nursery. So 'Library' means our Dining Room. 'Dining Room' means our Downstairs Bedroom. And 'Nursery' means my mother-and-father's room. But that bell never gets rung anyway.

Last of all on that wall comes the door to the Scullery.

Oh what a place is the Scullery!

As big as the Kitchen. With a concrete floor.

The brick wall outside the window, and no heating ever.

But I still love it! It's really truly homely, and no guests ever come into it.

It has . . . the mangle, dolly-tub, dumper, shoe-cleaning stuff, galoshes, wellington boots, grass-cutter, big tins of chicken-meal and corn, storm lantern, paraffin can and filler-funnel, sweeping brush and mop, an old table for mixing the chicken feed on, the vegetable box, a shallow stone sink with a cold-water tap, the galvanised buckets and the white enamel bucket, yellow kitchen soap, cloths and scrubbing brushes, the side door out to the dust-bins . . . and . . .

Three more *doors!*

That lead to three more *rooms!*

Well, one and two bits, anyway.

There's the Pantry, a little room you can walk into, with shelves all round, and very cool. Gauze over the window to keep out flies, so the sash can be left open to keep the jellies and custards and blancmanges cold. Tins for cakes and biscuits, all the home-made jam and marmalade, kilner-jars of bottled plums, bottles of milk, the big earthenware bread-crock on the floor in the corner, and the basin with eggs from the chickens.

The other two things in the Pantry are the big meat safe with a gauze door. And the mouse-traps on the shelves, which you have to check in the morning. I really hate it that we have to kill them, but there's nothing else for it. Sometimes, though, they get crafty, and you see a mouse sitting up on a shelf washing its whiskers, then scampering away behind the tins. The second of the three doors is for the Scullery Lavatory, just by the side door. Very handy when you pop in from cutting the grass or feeding the chickens, as no one minds about muddy boots. It's also, I hate to

96

mention, the place where the mice are got rid of.

And the third is . . . the Coal Cellar! We call it a cellar, though it's only down one step. But it is *huge!* There's a story in my old Milly-Molly-Mandy book about the coal cellar being turned into a bedroom for her. I can't really imagine being able to scrub and whitewash ours, like in the story, but it's certainly big enough for about three Milly-Molly-Mandys.

To fill up the coal scuttles from the Lounge or the Dining Room you go . . . along the Front Hall, down the three steps, along the passage, into the Kitchen, through the Kitchen and out again into the Scullery, straight across and open the Coal Cellar door, down one step, search around for the right-sized lumps or break up the gigantic ones with the coal hammer and . . . all the way back again. Phew!

The Coal Cellar has an extra L-shaped part, as big as the Linen Cupboard, that runs along behind the Pantry and has a shuttered coal-hole opening in the side passageway. My mother has to order a ton of coal at a time, and when the coalman comes it is *fantastic!* Like a glorious thunderstorm!

Rumble-rumble-bump-bang-crash . . . and rumbling on and on like exciting distant thunder as the coalmen tramp down the side passage, with leather pieces over their heads and shoulders, and tip twenty bags in through the coal-hole in the wall, and it comes roaring and tumbling down the L-shaped bit like a black river, wave after wave pouring into the cellar . . . and, "Keep the door shut, darling, for the dust!"

That reminds me . . .

Excuse me, I'll finish going round the Kitchen first. From the door into the Scullery and back down the right-hand wall to where I'm imagining me sitting at the kitchen table, is the gas cooker, the enamel-topped table (for putting bowls and things on when you're cooking), and the old range that my mother cooked on till a few years back, with wall cupboards either side.

All that part round about the old range is a bit special.

I'll save telling about it till later.

Because . . .

*   *   *   *

e

I was remembering. And thinking.

About the Kitchen being the place that belongs to *us*. The place that is *home*.

Sometimes, in a boarding-house, you feel you're almost tripping over people. You can't go anywhere in the whole place without meeting someone on the stairs and getting asked boring questions and having to give polite answers. If you escape to the Dining Room, it always seems to be time to clear away whatever you're doing, to set the table for the next meal.

Or - to do a great big *exaggeration* - I escape to the Dining Room and the Chimney Sweep arrives. Or disappear to wherever is my room, and there's the Window Cleaner waving through the window. Well, that's silly, I know. But it's the way I feel occasionally.

So the Kitchen is home, almost always. It could happen that things get too busy in the Kitchen. Time to get out from under people's feet. Escape to the Scullery to do some experiments with water, or pick dried grass off the mower blades, or even polish shoes in peace.

But . . . there's a knock on the side door, and it could be the . . .

Gas Meter Man, Electricity Man, Baker, Butcher, Fishmonger, Greengrocer, Chimney Sweep, the Chair-seat Mender, the Knife-Grinder to sharpen the scissors and the garden shears, or the Window Cleaner for more water.

Sometimes there are just too many people.

I'm having a think. Kitty Carter doesn't count as 'people'. She comes quite a lot of mornings to help with beds and baking and things for lunch, and it's as if she brings happiness with her. When Kitty's around, things sort themselves out with no fuss. And she never pesters or asks stupid questions or makes a Bother.

But there's another person who doesn't count as 'people', for quite a different reason. And that's another Rose, Rose Moody, who comes on two of the afternoons when Rose Walford isn't here, to clean the silver and brass. In the holidays I sometimes sit and clean it with her, which is why I can explain a bit about her and the reason why she's not 'people'.

If I say, "It's because she's Not All There," it might give you the wrong idea. It's true she sounds dotty, but she isn't really. What it is, is this:

She is here, but her mind is *there* - away in the past. She polishes away busily but doesn't pay any attention to me or anyone else, except the past people who live in her head and talk to her, and she talks back.

So of course that makes her another peaceful person who doesn't pester or make Bothers. She doesn't even make conversation, which is fine with me. I can polish away busily, too, and look around, and read interesting bits of the newspaper that we're polishing on, and think my own thoughts.

Rose Moody is tall and strange and wavery, and frequently flaps her hands around her head even when she's walking, like brushing away flies, to try and get rid of the past people. She is thin and bony and has fawny-grey hair done up on top, and a black dress and a little apron.

The first thing she does when she arrives, is put a slightly paraffin-smelling brown-paper parcel down on the end of the dresser behind the big soup tureen. Then hangs her raincoat on the kitchen hooks on the window wall, and takes all the hat-pins out of the sort of black bonnet that sits on top of her hair, and puts the hat and the pins by her parcel. Then lifts newspapers from the pile that we keep underneath the dresser, next to the tea-chest, and spreads them over half the kitchen table.

My mother is maybe doing ironing on the ironing-board, and asks, "Would you do the silver today, Rose, please?" and Rose always just says, "Yes M'. Very well, M'am!" and fetches the silver jug and teapot, milk jug and sugar bowl, the round silver biscuit barrel, the cruet stand, the mustard pot with the blue glass lining, and all the silver from the cutlery drawer, as well as the box of delicate fish knives and forks lying in blue velvet.

While she's lining them up on the newspaper, I fetch the cleaning stuff from the Scullery - the cloths and the old toothbrush for the fiddly bits, the Goddards Plate Powder, and the old saucer we use to put the powder on and mix it to a paste with water.

As long as Rose Moody has her hands free, like when she's walking or fetching things from a cupboard, she can wave her hands around and flap the past people away, and tells them out loud, "Go *away!* Stop *talking!*"

But once we settle down to work, they come back into her

brain.

They must have been horrible.

Rose polishes away at a spoon, furiously, as if she wants to polish it to pieces. Like when you're so mad you want to slam doors and throw things. Then she starts muttering, and awful bits of hating talk come through, saying, "You *devil!* . . . You damned *devil!* . . . mutter - mutter . . . Wicked bitch, that's what I say, wicked tarted-up old bitch . . . mutter - mutter . . . Devil take that blasted Lady Somebody - Lady Muck, I say, nothing but a damned hussy . . . mutter - mutter . . . No! No! You *devil* . . . I'll *kill* you! . . . mutter - mutter," . . . polish, polish, polish.

To begin with, my Mum would be very concerned for Rose, and ask what was the matter, and Rose would always answer, "It's the radio - the radio in my head - it won't stop."

So now we just ask, in a friendly way as if we're asking about a sick pet, "Is the radio bad today, then, Rose?" and she says, "Yes M', it's a bit bad today."

My mother says it isn't Rose talking. I mean, it's not her ideas or her thoughts, but only her mind repeating what she has heard. My Mum is fond of Rose (well, I am too, in a funny way) and sorry for her, and thinks she must have had a hard life and was probably a lady's maid to some high-up Society Lady. And that A Lot Goes On, that one would never know about.

But a lady's maid can't help hearing. And it won't go away. Poor Rose.

Rose Moody is very ladylike herself. And when the silver is all done, or the brass on brass-polishing day, she likes to serve Afternoon Tea in the Lounge. She insists on wearing her maid's frilly apron and cap that she's kept from the old days, and brings with her in her paraffiny brown-paper parcel. It's only the outside that's paraffiny. The frilly apron is quite nice.

And Rose stands up very straight, and carries the silver tray very properly and proudly.

It does make you think.

There are so many different kinds of people in the world.

And it makes you wonder what made them the way they are.

13

THE GARDEN IS A GOOD PLACE
FOR A LOT OF THINGS

It's a Sunday afternoon and we've all been in the garden playing cricket with a tennis ball.

Not Granpie, because he stays with Acton Grannie on Sunday afternoons. But my Dad and my brother and me, and Mr Grüning who enjoys cricket very much, and my Mum came out for a little while to be a fielder before she went for her Sunday rest. We persuaded Mr Sprigget, only it's not his sort of thing and he got l.b.w. pretty quickly. Mr Ashley, though, stayed with us all the time till he hit a terrific ball to boundary and it went over into Mr and Mrs Meredith's next door.

That's when the game packed in, because it took my brother and me so long to find it.

One reason for taking so long was that it's a mysterious Looking-Glass garden, all little paths like a maze, and archways and trellises of rustic poles with rambler roses and honeysuckle climbing and drooping all over them. There didn't seem to be anyone at home when we knocked at the back door, so we had a good look round.

The other reason is that we found where one of our Rhode Island Reds has been laying away. She'd made a sort of nest under Mr and Mrs Meredith's laurels down the bottom of their garden, and there were seven eggs in it. So we had to carry them over the wall, handing them across one at a time, and tell my father. That corner of the garden, opposite the chicken house, is easy to get over.

Not just for us. For the chickens, too. That's where the garden rubbish pile is. Even with their wings clipped, which you have to do, they only need to give a little jump and a flutter and they're over.

So now everyone's gone away.

My brother and I played catch for a bit, but we didn't really feel in the mood for it. And it doesn't feel like a day for digging tunnels together or mucking about with the old paint tins and bits of wood.

So he went off somewhere and I did various things, such as:

1. Had a look over the other corner of the bottom wall to see if Anna and her brother or the other two were in their gardens, but they weren't.
2. Collected three eggs from the chicken house egg-boxes.
3. Went to see how the pullets were getting on, that came from the day-old chicks my father got in a box, and are growing up in their own little house and run along the back wall.
4. Talked chicken talk to the hens for a bit, and found them some good worms.
5. Squashed some of the caterpillars on the gooseberry bush, which I get fed up with doing very quickly. Not that I'm specially fond of those caterpillars, but the gooseberry sort are so stinky, and there are millions of them.
6. Dead-headed the pansies in my bit of garden, to help them make more flowers, which are a lovely soft all-the-same-colour blue.
7. Picked some seed-heads off the hollyhocks, that are

102

like rolls of little pennies when you take them to pieces.

8. Started playing catch-and-clap-and-twist with myself on the house wall that's best for it, in the tucked-away bit of the L-shape where the steps go up to the Dining Room French windows. Till I remembered that Miss Fazackerly would be trying to have a Sunday Afternoon Nap, just on the other side of where my ball was bouncing.

9. Stopped playing catch, which I wasn't feeling much like anyway, and tried to see how long I could balance on the garden roller.

10. Chose some good broad Plantain leaves, which there are plenty of on the grass, as well as clover, and picked out the bits in between the ribs to make them into leaf-skeleton banjos.

Since then I've just been lying on my back chewing grass and doing nothing.

When I was doing most of these things I was also doing a lot more thinking.

I mean, the thinking was just happening.

Not the six-things-at-once-like-a-layer-cake. But the string-of-beads sort, when one thought leads to another and another and another. It's amazing where you end up.

Or when you've ended up, you think: Now how did all that start? and you follow the thought-beads backwards to find out.

Thinking! Ho hum!

I'll tell about some of it in a minute, but first I've got to put down a sort-of-poem I was making up, before I forget it. What I call a sort-of-poem is not as good as a poetry-think, but . . . well, anyway . . .

Tall gables zig-zag in the sky,
High, like a great fence.
What's on the other side?
More houses, and the odd tree.

Where is the country that we cannot see?
. . . But birds fly free.

Brick walls, old and red,
But high,
Make sure that we can't pry.
But why?
Why can't we see?
. . . But birds fly free.

Birds are wonderful.

My father says they are very . . . special. He says it like that.
They have a magic, airy life, so different from ours. But I think
he means more than that . . . as if they're a wondrous mystery
. . . mysterious spirits.

It does make you wonder. When a robin alights by your spade,
and cocks his eye and looks at you. Or when the swifts, at
evening, wheel and scream round the chimneys and whizz along
invisible switch-backs in the air.

It's very sleepy-summery just now.

A few little white clouds are floating up in the blue. The haws
are beginning to come on the may tree, and a titchy-tiny green
caterpillar is letting himself down off a branch on a long gos-
samer thread.

I can hear a bumble bee buzzing over on the hollyhocks - in
fact I can see him, he's getting so pollen-covered he'll have a job
taking off.

There's someone talking quietly, just now and then, over the
wall. Not the Meredith's - the other side, where Miss Perry is such
a good gardener.

And there's a wood pigeon coo-cooing somewhere.

If you startle them, wood pigeons fly out of a tree with a great
clap. But ordinary pigeons, when they soar above the garden,
look as if they're doing it for fun. They go flap-flap-flap very
straight upwards until they're high enough, like climbing steep
steps up to the top diving board. And then let go, and swoop in a
fantastically marvellous curve like an expert doing a swallow-

dive, and go swimming through the air as if it's a blue sea.

This thinking I was going to tell you about, I've followed the thought-beads back to see where it started. So here goes:

The garden is a relief. Like when my mother gets a minute to put her feet up, and says, "Oh, that's a relief!"

Sometimes it's all a bit much, them being there all the time. And trying to understand them, and why they're the way they are. All of us so separate and not-understanding, like walls between us. Yet always someone making a Bother, or wanting things, or ask-ask-asking.

So I didn't think about it any more, only that it was nice being in the garden on my own.

At school there's a garden out the back, with grass where we play Statues at break-time, and cherry trees with leaves that turn a wonderful red. In autumn it's like walking through drifts of jewels and flames and you can't bear not to pick them up and keep them. So I do, and use the best for book marks.

That, and our English teacher, are the only two good things, and I think . . . well, I begin to get the suspicion . . . that I go to a pretty silly school.

I can't tell for sure, as it's the only one I've been to except for kindergarten, but . . .

Can you believe it? We have to wear white gloves on the street, even on the way to school, and get reported if someone notices us not wearing them. And in summer it's white cotton piqué dresses, and if you get ink on them when your nib splutters, it won't wash out, only goes brown.

We're always practising dancing, to do for the parents at the Christmas Ball. And we don't do drawing, only embroidery and making jewellery and stuffed toys. And we started Algebra last term, but all we've done is pages and pages of diagrams of weighing scales, with fruit or books or whatever we like on them, balancing each other. It's supposed to be to do with equations, but it doesn't make sense to me.

I used not to think like this.

I thought that must be what school is meant to be.

But now, I wonder.

I could read and write and do sums before I came to this

school. And anything interesting I've found out since, has been from Granpie, or from reading Mr Ashley's *National Geographics* and Mr Grüning's Kiplings, and getting books from the library.

The only other things worth mentioning at school are Parsing Sentences, which we do all the time, and Latin stuff like Nominative, Accusative, Dative, and amo, amas, amat out of a little book. You'd think there must be something else to learn?

The other thing I start wondering, is why I go to it. Why that one, I mean, and not the ordinary school? It's Granpie who decides about schools, I think, though I don't know for sure. The only thing I can work out, is this:

Most of the people in these streets must be rich, I suppose, to have such big houses all to themselves. And we have a big house because we're poor, to Make Ends Meet with the boarders. But perhaps if you have a big house you have to go to a rich persons' silly school, instead of going to a sensible ordinary school where you don't have to wear stupid white gloves.

Is that why?

Perhaps somebody knows. But I don't.

There are too many things I don't know.

This is still me, following the string-of-beads thoughts.

The next one was another silly thing at school that I remembered while I was at the bottom of the garden talking to the chickens.

My fire-lighting test!

I joined the school Guide Company this year and one of the tests for my Tenderfoot Badge was 'light a fire with one match' on the path in the school garden. And would you believe it? All they asked me to do was light some paper in between two bricks and chuck a heap of dead leaves onto it, off the rubbish pile! It lit beautifully and went out in about six seconds.

And I passed!

That can't be right.

Pauline in my class says I should join the Company she's in, that's nothing to do with a school, because they do Morse and Semaphore and go camping.

So maybe I will.

106

Why does it take so long to explain what a thought was?

I only remembered the fire-lighting thing for about one second, because being down the bottom of our garden reminded me. The moment I thought it, my brain said 'Guides'. And the minute it said 'Guides' I was away dreaming and remembering and thinking about the thing they call Divisional Church Parade, that happened last week.

They only have it once a year, and all the Guide Companies from all around go to it, and the Colour Parties carry the flags up to the altar.

I can't stop thinking about it, it was so amazingly marvellous.

Nothing like that has ever happened to me before.

I'd never even been in a church like that before.

Granpie came this morning, the way he does every Sunday morning before he goes back to Acton Grannie, and took me to church round the corner where we always go. We sit in the gallery because when I was little he could sneak me out before the sermon without disturbing anyone. I like singing hymns, but there's nothing to look at except the minister in a black gown, and the tops of people's heads down below, and all the different sorts of hats which I must admit I spend quite a lot of time counting when the talking goes on too long.

I don't know how to explain what I'm thinking without sounding silly, but the *shape* of the church we go to is wrong. It doesn't have a meaning. There's just the minister looking at the people, and people looking at the minister, and woodwork all around, and that's it. Finish.

But . . .

This other church . . .

The roof goes up and up into wonderful shapes and shadows, so that you can imagine it doesn't really stop at the roof but goes on up into other places . . . and shafts of light coming through . . . it makes you think, "O ye spirits and souls of the righteous, bless ye the Lord . . . "

And the end with the place they call the altar has a going-on feel to it, as if *it* doesn't stop either . . . as if the eyes in your head are seeing the colours and shapes, but the eyes in your mind are looking right through it and keeping on going . . . like Space and

107

Eternity and God.

And this place that doesn't stop but keeps going on and on into Eternity is where all our flags were taken.

But the flags mean *us,* I think.

We've taken ourselves up there. And put ourselves there, in that place.

I can't think much more of this, or I'll go dizzy.

I didn't think like this when I was there. I was too amazed by everything.

I didn't know there *were* so many Guides. Hundreds and hundreds of us, all singing together, and then all very quiet together. It was terribly solemn, but very very happy.

I've never known anything like it.

It was like being by myself only more so.

Or as if all of us weren't separate any more, but all one.

I don't remember anything that was said, except that it seemed to make sense. But, the singing . . . oh, the singing! It was like being part of a great big wonderful wave, swinging and swooping along and curving up and over. Especially in the one that went:

> 'Over the hills and the sea-girt coast,
> Over the billows of blue,
> Rings out a call from the Lord of Hosts
> Sent to the brave and true . . .'

which had the most fantastically marvellous tune, like people all happy together, joining hands and dancing through the streets.

I *think* it was made up by Guides in Poland, but I'm not sure.

The other one we had was *I Vow to Thee, My Country*, which had a good tune too. I didn't like the words of the first verse much, but the other verse is very special. And very quiet. We were allowed to bring the hymn sheets home with us, so I've learned it off by heart.

> 'And there's another country, I've heard of long ago,
> Most dear to them that love her, most great to them
>   that know;
> We may not count her armies; we may not see her king;

Her fortress is a faithful heart, her pride is suffering;
And soul by soul and silently her shining bounds increase,
And her ways are ways of gentleness and all her paths
are peace.'

I don't know why I like it so much.

Perhaps it's because it makes me think of Devonshire Grannie.

And my mother, too. Because she is so faithful and gentle and her name means peace.

But . . .

Here's what I'm lying on the grass thinking about - this funny-peculiar business of feeling separate and not feeling separate.

How is it that I can find *nine* other people All-A-Bit-Much-Sometimes. And find *hundreds* of people like Being-By-Myself-Only-More-So?

Now there *is* a puzzle.

I'm *very* glad it's nearly tea-time.

14

KITTENS AND THINGS

I can remember when my mother cooked on the old range.

She uses the gas cooker now, as it's less tiring and not so baking hot in summer. But the range is still there and still looks exactly the same.

The range is big and black and handsome. It stands on red quarry tiles in an alcove lined with tiles that are shining white like dinner plates, and its black chimney goes up and into a black tin plate in the alcove ceiling.

There's a place in the top for the coal, a pull-down flap to see if the fire is glowing nicely behind the bars, and an oven with shelves that are flat trays.

Then of course there's the coal hod, and the tall fire-irons leaning in the corner, and the elegant black cast-iron fender along the front of the red tiles.

That fender used to be so handy for drying shoes.

Either side of the range alcove are green-painted cupboard doors, a top and a bottom one on each side, with wooden shelves that go away back into the wall. My mother white-washes the

110

insides of the cupboards every year, very clean-looking, but it comes off white on your hands.

The right-hand cupboards have things like the stuff for black-leading the range, and the old flat irons that we used to heat up on the range and then put into their smooth 'shoe' to iron the clothes, and also the new electric iron.

The left-hand cupboards have all the baking things at the top, like sweetie-jars of flour, the sultanas and currants, and golden syrup and black treacle. And at the bottom, the weighing scales and rolling pin, pastry board and cutters. Also the big heavy mincer that we screw onto the kitchen table, for making the left-overs of the Sunday joint into cottage pie for Mondays. And the marmalade cutter that has a sort of guillotine blade inside, and a wooden handle on top that you push from side to side quickly, while with the other hand you shove an orange up against it and keep on pushing until it all comes out the other side in thin slices and tons of juice.

It's a sticky job.

Juicy, anyway. It gets onto everything.

I forgot to mention the big long airer with cast-iron ends and long wooden rails, that lets down on a rope. I don't know what we'd do without that. Even now, without the range on, there's enough heat in the Kitchen to finish off drying things when we fetch them in from the garden.

Half the time, though, it's full up with things like my wet mackintosh and hat and satchel when I get back from school.

It's an interesting walk, coming from school.

There's the place where you can watch the trains, the tank-engines on the slow line, and the great big speeding exciting always-in-a-hurry main-line locomotives with their smoke flowing out all the way down the line of carriages.

And there are the Baths, that always smell of chlorine, even outside. And the Council Stables, and the shire horses pulling the two-wheeled wooden carts with the slats at the side, coming back from working at the park or the roads.

It's quite a long way, though, and you can get pretty wet.

So the Kitchen was specially comfortable to come back to and get your tea in, when the range was on.

*   *   *   *

111

Once upon a time there was a stray tabby cat who used to stalk up and down between the kitchen window and the nasturtium patch, looking fierce and ferocious.

If we called it or went, "Puss! Puss!" it ran away, but came back again next day.

My mother started putting a saucer of milk out every morning and calling, "Come, Tiddles!" Sure enough, once she went inside the house again, Tiddles would come and lap it up so fast that drops of milk would jump out of the saucer, but looking up all the time as if to say, "You dare! You just try!"

If my mother tried to go near while she was drinking, Tiddles hissed and spat, and bristled her whiskers and put her ears back, just like a wild cat.

But never, ever, did she go far away or stop prowling up and down outside.

So perhaps she knew that she was going to need a home, very soon.

How is it that memories start?

Why is there just one moment, like drawing a line across your life with a ruler, and before that moment you remember nothing and after it you remember everything?

I don't remember Tiddles prowling, and my mother putting out saucers of milk, only what I've been told.

But I do, very very clearly, remember Tiddles curled up in an old box in the Kitchen with all her little kittens.

And everything after that.

To the left of the range and to the left of the left-hand cupboards, is a sticking-out bit of wall that makes a tucked-away cosy corner. It is out of the draughts, and gets light from the window and warmth from the range.

That's where Tiddles had her box and lay curled up with her kittens. Two were tabby like her, two were black and one was ginger. Their eyes were shut and they mewled with little faint, feeble voices.

It's a very long time ago but I can remember how Tiddles would come out of her box to eat food put down for her under the

112

enamel-topped work table by the gas stove, just next to her box. And she'd also leave her kittens for a little while, to go out through the Scullery and into the garden when she needed to.

But if you tried to go near, to touch her or the kittens, she still hissed and spat and was still a wild cat.

I remember being allowed to choose which kitten we were going to keep. It was the ginger one and we called him Marmalade. I don't know where Tiddles went after that. But I remember my Dad in his saggy old fawn raincoat and grey hat, going up and down the road and off round the houses with the rest of the kittens in a brown paper carrier bag to find good homes for them.

We had Marmalade until last summer when we found him stretched out under the front privet hedge as stiff as a stuffed cat. I was told he must have been poisoned. He was a very solid cat, not particularly friendly or cuddly. So although I was sorry, I didn't feel the same as when Tigger died.

The kittens being born was when I was four.

I remember just about everything after that, including my baby brother being born the same year.

I was glad to have a baby brother.

But I wasn't at all curious about where he had come from.

My mother had him in a Nursing Home and I was taken to visit them, so perhaps I thought that's where you went to collect your new baby. I didn't know what being born meant, only that new things arrived.

There are so many other interesting things to do, I never bothered to think about it. And I know now that things are born from their mothers - you sort of pick that up from books - but I don't know *how*. It's only recently that I've started wondering about it and feeling so stupid and ignorant, not knowing. And once it's started, the need to know gets bigger and bigger until your mind feels bursting, and the question gets harder and harder to ask.

I managed to work myself up to it last week.

My Mum and I were clearing up in the Dining Room after a meal. We'd just folded the starched linen tablecloth, which is a two-man job, and I managed to blurt out, "Do please tell me . . . *how* are babies born?"

She turned round from putting the cloth away in the sideboard drawer, and tears began to come into her eyes the way they do with anything wonderful or mysterious, or that she's shy about.

She asked, "Don't you know?" and her voice was loving and gentle.

I shook my head, feeling lost and upset.

So she said, "Why, my darling, the same way as kittens . . . the way that kittens are born."

My mother wasn't meaning to put me off. She said it as if she was telling me everything there was to know. As if she was saying, "Yes my darling, I *want* you to know, and this is how it is."

But . . . I don't *know* how kittens are born. I've never seen it happen and no one has told me.

And I can't ask any more. Getting one question past my teeth was difficult enough.

I wish *saying things* was easier.

Do grown-ups have a secret list in their minds, of things you don't talk about?

It'd be a whole lot easier if they wrote it out and stuck it up for people to see, with a list of books to get from the library and look up the answers in, so as not to speak.

Take all these pretend sayings they have about going to the lavatory. My father says he's 'Going-To-See-A-Man-About-A-Dog'. My Aunt Marjorie says she's 'Paying-A-Visit'. Or that she's 'Going-To-See-George'. Where does she get that idea?

And now that I'm not a baby any more I'm supposed to say that 'I Want-To-Be-Excused'.

But it makes you feel . . . well, sort of awfully *cautious.*

As if you've got to be dreadfully careful.

In case the wrong words come out of your mouth by accident.

Talking of sayings.

I like Granpie's one, when we're doing one of his favourite making and mending jobs together, and he says, "Never spoil the ship for a hap'orth of tar."

And my father, supposing I'm down helping him with the

chickens and I get in his way, he'll burst out with, "Let the dog see the rabbit!"

But supposing he's trying to hit a nail in, which he's not very good at, and hits his thumb instead, if he's only hurt a little bit he'll go, "Acha!" But if it's a good big wallop, he spits out, "Acha-Polka-Mazaria!" and shakes his thumb in the air to cool it down.

No one knows what it means!

It sounds like a good old Witchy-Wizardy Spell!

15

THE DINING ROOM

Mr Ashley has left.

Perhaps he has got a house of his own. Or maybe he's gone to be a dentist in another town.

I don't know.

What is hard to explain to anyone who isn't used to living in a boarding-house, is that you don't ever think about why people leave. It doesn't enter your head, you get so used to guests coming and going. One month someone's there, and the next they're gone.

Room-Next-to-the-Tank-Cupboard boarders don't usually stay more than a few months. Mr Ashley's been with us a lot longer than Mr Hughes or Mr Muller or Mr Dupré or any of the others.

And . . .

I don't know how you're going to believe this. But it's true.

He's left me *all his National Geographics!*

I can still hardly believe it myself. I feel like the richest person on earth.

I don't mean he just left them behind in his room. He told me.

It was last night when I was turning the handle of the sewing machine for my mother. He tapped on the Dining Room door and put his head round the corner and asked if he could come in and have a word. He explained that he was leaving, which I knew because my Mum had just told me, and then he said, "And I don't really want to take the *Geographics*, I've read them all and I know you'll enjoy them - would you like to have them?"

Well!

I feel as if that was the biggest '*thank you!*' of my life. Now I don't have to rush to finish them. I can take my time, read them twice over, copy the pictures . . . anything! I can even take them to school for Geography, which will be a heap more interesting than the fiddly little sketch-maps we have to take it in turn to borrow and bring home to copy out with a mapping pen.

I'm useless with mapping pens. They're so scratchy, they catch on the paper and spray blots all over it.

Anyway, then Mr Ashley asked my Mum whether he should bring the *Geographics* down, or leave them where they are. And she said thank you, and would he please leave them in the cupboard because the Room Next to the Tank Cupboard is going to be my room again for a bit.

This changing rooms is another thing you don't bother to ask the 'why' of. It's like moving pieces on a draughts board. There's always a reason for moving but the reason is often too complicated to explain.

For instance, it could be that my brother is to go in the Linen Cupboard now, instead of in my mother-and-father's room. On the other hand it may turn out to be that my brother and I are to share the Room Next to the Tank Cupboard because the Linen Cupboard is needed for something else.

Maybe as a dressing-room for my mother. After she has cooked the evening dinner but before she serves it up, she always changes into one of her beautiful dresses that she's had for ever and ever. But she gets tired. And it's a long way for her to go all the way up to the top of the house to change.

So that could be the reason.

But I haven't been moved yet. I'll find out soon enough.

When you first put your head round the Dining Room door, you think, 'A Grand Piano! What on earth is a Grand Piano doing in a Dining Room?'

And not just any old Grand Piano either, but the largest size there is, the sort they use on concert platforms. It belongs to my mother and is the one part of her old life that she will *not* give up for anything. When things get to be a Bit Too Much, and she feels like letting go and letting rip, she comes in and accompanies herself at the piano and sings her heart out. If it's meant to be soft, she sings softly. But if it's meant to be fortissimo she gives it full resonance and full lung-power, and lets out a glorious wave of contralto song loud enough to fill a concert hall.

At the moment the piano is still in its summer position. It takes up the whole of the left-hand side of the long fireplace wall, with its foot at the mantelpiece and the keyboard up at the window, and just room for a chair. That way we can still open the French windows (which are double doors with glass in them) and go down the steps into the garden.

But any day now it will start getting chilly enough to light the Cosy-Stove, the black stove with fire-doors that open, and little mica windows to see the glow through. Once it's lit, it stays alight all the rest of the autumn and winter, and the lovely polished wood of the foot of the piano would get scorched.

So we move the piano! What a job!

It takes three people to swivel it round and shift it to its winter position across the French windows and the side windows.

It takes up the whole end of the room and sticks out quite a long way, too.

There's enough space left in the middle of the room for our big solid dining table - which is also our dressmaking-and-sewing-and-painting-and-homework table - with ten chairs tucked in round it.

But it's a bit of a squash when it comes to putting the extra leaf in the table and playing table tennis. We stack up the chairs all round the room, and scrabble underneath and crawl under the piano to get the ball back. And my Dad, who is tall, has to watch out for the furniture when he does smashes and spins.

When you first put your head round the Dining Room door you'd also notice the wireless sitting on the piano up the fireplace end.

118

And up above it, the picture of the lady whose eyes follow you wherever you go. It's just a print of a calm and noble sort of person in a filmy cream dress, with brown trees behind. But it's life-size. And she does stare, in a very considering sort of way.

For a moment you might even think there's a real person there, looking at you silently and wondering who you are and what you're like.

Then you pull your eyes away and on the right of her you'd immediately be magicked by the wonder of the overmantel. It is fixed to the wall above the mantelpiece, and towers up to the high picture-rail . . . an oval mirror set in a carved and polished wood frame that curves and swirls like little waves blowing onto a pebbly beach . . . and tiny rounded shelves delicately poised two on each side and one along the top, set with the loveliest small china pieces, like the dolls' teapot with flower decorations, two dainty cups and saucers, and a tiny vase of unglazed china like thin bone.

I'm allowed to dust it all, standing on a chair and reaching high to take down each piece separately onto the table.

To the right of the fireplace is the sideboard where we put the trays and my mother carves and dishes up the meal. And coming back down the right-hand wall, between the sideboard and the door, is a gigantically huge chest-of-drawers that goes almost up to the ceiling. The drawers are six feet wide, and deep, and on either side of them are hanging-cupboards like tall sentry-boxes with doors, which are great hide-and-seek places when you get in behind the coats.

All the drawers have names. They are the Top Drawer, the Linen Drawer, the Music Drawer, the Toy Drawer and the Mending Drawer. The Music Drawer is so full of oratorios and song books and hundreds and hundreds of pieces of sheet music, you can hardly pull the drawer open for the weight of it, and the handles keep coming off and have to be glued on again.

On the other side of the wall that this chest-of-drawers thing is on is the Downstairs Bedroom.

And I'll tell you a thing . . . we've got someone new in there.

Mrs W has gone and life is a whole lot pleasanter. The doctor said she ought to be in a home where they have a Matron and nurses, because of her blood pressure.

Three cheers!

So now we have Mrs Ritchie who is a chirpy wee thing, and so small and birdlike you could pick her up with one hand. She is old, and does her grey hair up on top the way they all do, and wears a long black skirt, a black lace blouse and a black wool shawl fastened with a gold brooch. But she is good company and a bit of a tease and keeps us lively.

And I'll tell you something . . .

My Mum says, "What a relief!" At last she's got someone she can have a laugh with!

For instance, Mrs Ritchie has a habit of staggering and putting out a hand to steady herself against the wall, to show how fragile she is and that a puff of wind would blow her away. It's not real. She's acting. But it's good acting, and she'd be disappointed if no one took any notice.

So that gives my Mum the chance to tease her and say something like, "Ah, Mrs Ritchie, you've been having a little drink on the sly!" or even just, "Hallo, are you propping up the wall again?"

And that pleases them both and they have a little laugh together. It's just silly nonsense, as my Mum says. But the whole house feels happier.

What a difference one person can make.

Once upon a time when I was little, Granpie and I used to play with matchbox boats in the bath. We'd fix a paper sail onto a matchstick and set it into the lid of the empty box. Granpie would cut off a tiny piece of camphor, that you get little squares of at the chemist for putting in your hankie and sniffing when you've got a cold, and fix the piece of camphor into a nick in the back of the boat.

Then we'd fill the bath with water, kneel down beside it and carefully lower the matchbox onto the surface and . . . let go! Phweee! The camphor fizzed in the water, and the boat went . . . all the way down the bath and all the way back again if you turned it round.

*   *   *   *

120

I think Mrs Ritchie's like the camphor. She fizzes, and things start moving.

Even the conversation at table has perked up. Especially between Mrs Ritchie and Miss Elphin who seem to be quite two of a kind once they get talking about the Old Days and When They Were Young, and skating on ponds with hot potatoes inside their muffs to keep their hands from freezing.

Can you believe it! It's hard to imagine Miss Elphin being young and daring, with red cheeks and her scarf flying out behind her.

Perhaps Miss Fazackerly finds it hard to believe, too. Or else maybe she never had that sort of fun. I wish she would chatter away like the other two. It's sad really . . . whatever she says seems to come out sounding a bit snobbish, even if she doesn't mean it . . . like talking about Good Upbringing and Chaperones.

I asked her what a Chaperone was, because I don't know, and she snapped, "Children should be Seen-and-not-Heard!"

Then when they started talking about picnic parties and who they went with, Mrs Ritchie gave Miss Elphin a dig in the ribs and said in a loud whisper, "I believe you had an Admirer!"

Well!

Miss Elphin actually smiled and blushed! And opened her mouth to come out with an answer, but Miss Fazackerly chipped in quickly with, "Little-Pitchers-Have-Big-Ears!"

I know what *that* means . . . and it's not *fair!* Because they all shut up, and now I'll never know.

However, I dare say Miss Fazackerly thought the conversation was Getting-Out-of-Hand. Even Mr Grüning, who likes a chuckle, was going, "Hrmmph!" behind his napkin.

But . . .

I *think* that if Mrs Ritchie stays with us for long enough, and keeps on trying, Miss Fazackerly will get to be more human in the end. Especially if I keep quiet so that they forget I'm there.

Because Mrs Ritchie has sauce enough for anything. Although she's a little old lady she is like a small child, in the nicest way. She's so tiny, she can be cheeky and get away with it. And if there's something she wants to say, she says it straight out without thinking twice.

There's something nice that happened the other night because of her, but first I want to tell a bit more about dinner-times, and my mother dressing for dinner, and about her being tired.

She does get tired. Very tired. And has blinding headaches at times, and varicose veins from standing at the stove.

Even in the evenings she can't stop because of the sewing. Every night when she's finished in the Kitchen, it's up onto the dining table with the old Frister & Rossman sewing machine, that was Devonshire Grannie's and is so handsome with the gold scrollwork along its black shining sides.

If it's long straight seams like sides-to-middling sheets, when my homework's done I can whir away at the handle as fast as galloping horses, while my Mum guides the material and calls, "Whoa!" when we're getting near the end of a seam or if the spool needs rewinding or the thread breaks or snarls up.

But quite often it's stuff that's too difficult for me to help with, like dress-making from paper patterns, or altering a skirt that's been handed down, or running up costumes that my silly school says we've to have for a dancing display.

I don't know why we have to, but we do.

And it's not fair on my Mum, who has enough to do without that.

I don't even like dancing.

But that's the way it is. Greek costume is easy - all you need to do is dye an old piece of sheet mauve, and drape it over one shoulder. However, the year we did the *Something About a Soldier* song-and-dance, my mother had to make blue cotton trousers and stitch gilt braid up the seams, and a red cotton jacket with shiny buttons, and attach a chin-strap elastic to a round cheese-box and paint it red to make a pill-box hat. All for half-an-hour's performance.

All that work. And for what?

When it's finished with, the costume gets shoved in the dressing-up trunk, or folded and put in the Mending Drawer in case it comes in useful.

It's often very late at night before my mother can go to bed. When she does, she sits up and thinks out menus and writes the grocery order - I know, because she told me, and I asked, "Why not do it downstairs?" and she said, "It doesn't work like that, my darling, there's always another job waiting to be done."

So you can see why she gets tired.

She doesn't *act* tired. I mean, she's a cheerful worker, and enthusiastic about things, and Puts-A-Good-Face-On-It.

Perhaps that's why she makes a special effort with the evening meal, called 'dinner'. It's the main meal of the day. Even though my father is usually up at Covent Garden for the evening performance, my brother and I are home from school, and Mr Sprigget back from work (and Mr Ashley, too, until today), so it's quite a tableful.

When my Dad's there as well, it's four of us down each side and one at each end. The beautiful old starched damask cloth is shining white, the silver is gleaming and the glass cruet bottles are sparkling. In the centre is maybe one lovely just-uncurling peach-and-cream bud and spray of glossy-dark leaves from the Madam Butterfly rose bush, in a long-stemmed glass vase.

And my mother, who a few minutes before was red-faced over the cooker, has powdered her nose and dressed for dinner.

I suppose she bought the dresses before I was born, when she was a singer.

They're not modern clothes.

I'm glad they're not. There couldn't be any more beautiful.

She looks like a magic princess in a fairy tale. There's the dark-blue, gold-rose-patterned voile, the floaty mauve chiffon, and the dark blue linen with the waist-line down round her hips, and cuffs and collar embroidered with red and gilt thread.

But best of all is the sleeveless black velvet with a gauzy black-and-green chiffon blouse underneath. It has very full sleeves, tight again at the wrists, and so filmy-thin you can see the paleness of her arms. With it she wears the long diamanté chain that my Dad gave her when they were married. It hangs down on the black velvet in a long V, and looks like the dewdrops that sparkle on a spider's web after a misty morning.

That's what she was wearing the other night, a night when my Dad was home and we were all there.

The guests had just started on cheese and biscuits, and I was thinking of saying, "Please may I get down?" the way I'm supposed to, when Mrs Ritchie - who'd been with us a week or so - called up the table to my mother, "How about a tune then?

Will you sing us a song to cheer us up?"

There was a startled silence. I suppose they were all too polite ever to have thought of asking.

Then Mr Grüning rose to his feet, wiped his mouth with his napkin, ducked his head towards my mother, and made a *speech!* Like this:

"I do believe, Madam, that Mrs Ritchie has been brave enough to put into words what we have all long felt. I am sure I speak for the assembled company in saying that we should be *greatly honoured* if you would . . . if you would *both* . . . sing for us."

And he bowed first to my mother, then to my father at the other end of the table, and sat down. And the guests all clapped and said things like, "Yes, indeed!" and, "How delightful!" and, "That would be excellent!" and, "Hear, Hear!"

Well!

My mother was dimpling and going pink with pleasure. But then she stood up and began stacking the side plates, saying in her practical way, "Well, if you all stay here we'll make haste with the washing-up and see what we can do."

My brother helped carry things through to the Kitchen and then went back to keep the boarders company, because he's still only little and it was getting past his bedtime. My mother and father did the washing-up together and had a bit of a consultation, while I finished clearing up and made the coffee in the percolator. My mother took the cups in and we started.

They must have decided to keep it short, with it getting late and us all sitting on the dining chairs. So we didn't have *Bois Epais* or *Caro Mio Ben* or any of those. Just *I Must Go Down to the Seas Again,* and my mother's lovely and gentle *I Passed By Your Window.* Then she played *Oh, No John* for us all to join in the chorus, and they finished with their duet *Madam, Will You Walk?* as a treat for Mrs Ritchie, who had whispered to my Mum that she liked romantic ones.

It was a bit like a nice dream. We'd never all been so jolly together, ever before, except at Christmas-times.

Yet here it was, happening.

All because Mrs Ritchie had asked.

So now there's my father singing the verses where the grand gentleman with the haughty voice offers the lady a silken gown, a coach and six white horses if only she will walk and talk with

124

him.

And there's my mother, playing the piano all the time and looking beautiful in her black velvet and chiffony sleeves and dewdrop chain, glancing up with sparkling eyes and teasing looks and telling him that however many gifts he offers - No, she will *not* walk, and - No, she will *not* talk - No, she *will* not walk or talk with him!

Now my father's voice changes. He stops being haughty and rich and proud and sings pleadingly, "I will give you the Keys of my Heart, and we'll be married till death us do part . . .

> Madam, will you walk?
> Madam, will you talk?
> Madam, will you walk?
> and talk . . .
> with *me?*"

and the answer comes from my mother in a voice that is so full and happy as she sings the 'Yes' verse, you can tell that all she longed for has come true, she's just been waiting for him to come to his senses and say it right, and now everything in the whole wide world is wonderful.

Well, they sang the last verse together and then everyone was clapping, and Mrs Ritchie dabbing her eyes and murmuring, "How lovely!" But then my mother, who was beginning to stretch out her hand to fold down the music rest and shut the lid, looked a trifle anxiously at the other two ladies.

She's always a bit sorry for these old ones who have never married and had children. Miss Elphin had snoozed off. Miss Fazackerly, however, was sitting ram-rod straight as usual, but with one arm round my little brother who had fallen asleep against her shoulder. And my mother asked, "Was there something special you'd like me to play, Miss Fazackerly?"

Miss Fazackerly cleared her throat. She has a way of doing it that makes you think she's maybe quite shy, underneath her sharpness. She cleared her throat and said hesitatingly, in not at all her usual voice, "I believe you sometimes sing *The Lost Chord* . . . "

Her voice trailed off. I could feel my mother being doubtful inside. It's one of the ones she lets rip on, just once in a while, and a heavy one to play so late in the evening, with great giant chords and octaves marching up and down the keys.

But she went over to the Music Drawer and found it, and came back, saying, "I'll play it softly."

It is a strange song. Strange and wonderful. It has an eerie feel to begin with, very quiet and listening, as if something haunting is going to come . . .

"Seated one day at the organ I was weary and ill at ease,
And my fingers wandered idly over the noisy keys;
I know not what I was playing, or what I was dreaming then,
But I struck one chord of music like the sound of a great
Amen."

So my mother started softly, but soon the music swelled out, following the song. Sometimes it was quiet and sad, and 'trembled away into silence', and the musician thinks he has lost this beautiful sound. And sometimes it was joyful and glorious, like the ending, when it says:

"It may be that only in Heav'n . . .
I shall hear that grand Amen."

And Miss Fazackerly said quietly, "Thank you, that was beautiful!" and we all went to bed.

16

THE THING TO DO IS CARRY ON AS USUAL

The week after Mr Ashley left I got moved, right enough. You can never be sure till it happens, but . . . here I am!

The Room Next to the Tank Cupboard is my own room again. I'm back on the top landing next to the hissing old Tank Cupboard, the spooky place, the yo-yo place and the three steps up to my mother-and-father's room.

It's years and years since this was my room.

My mind knows that it's the smallest of the proper bedrooms.

But it *feels* absolutely colossally *huge* after the Linen Cupboard. Acres of cold floor all round the bed. Gallons of cold air floating up to the ceiling. Hundreds of draughts whee-ing out under the door to the roof and whistling round my head.

Not that the cold bothers me. It's like my Dad says, "Tuck down and let the gale blow over you!"

But it is very different from the Linen Cupboard. I was so tightly fitted into the Linen Cupboard it was like being wrapped round with an eiderdown, or someone holding onto you and keeping you safe, down there in the middle of the house.

Here, you're high up at the top of the house. On your own in the middle of empty spaces. I never noticed it like that before.

However, it still feels like my own place. Woofie is back on the mantelpiece with my dog collection round him, and Wrightie's gnome pictures on the walls. The *Geographics* are in the cupboard like a golden treasure-house. And the tulip curtains are still there . . . my night-sky-blue-with-parrots-in-a-jungle.

I'm glad I can still see them like that.

I can lie in bed and watch the pale light going grey behind the patterns.

And then going dark.

Maybe my brain will start going dizzy thinking about Space and Eternity.

And maybe it won't.

I'll have to wait and see.

There are so many other puzzling things these days . . . especially people. The thoughts I used to have when I was little, and still do have sometimes, are still the most interesting. Well, more than interesting . . . totally incredibly amazing. But you sort of get used to having those thoughts around - about Space going on and on for ever and things like that. You know you can take those thoughts out and look at them again, but you're not likely to come up with any answers. So most of the time you stop puzzling about them, and leave them alone.

But . . . people!

And the way things are.

It takes a lot of thinking about, to make any sense of it.

I went to a birthday party the day before yesterday.

There are two sorts of people at our school, the ones who have parties and the ones who don't.

None of my real friends have parties. There's May and Edna over the wall at the bottom of the garden, and Pauline that I walk half way with every morning, and quite a few others. I maybe get asked to tea at their houses sometimes, which is very nice. I wish I could ask people to tea, but I can't. Or else sometimes I just go round after school for a bit, like when I went to the Beckett twins' flat on the way home, and their mother was out, and we ate spoonfuls of Ovaltine out of the tin and crunched it up with ice-cubes from their huge big fridge. Fantastic! I'd never even seen a fridge before, not even a little one. And I'd never eaten an ice-cube. I'd never seen one, either. I suppose we're very old-fashioned.

Anyway . . . parties.

I suppose I'm being stupid, pretending I know anything about people who give parties, because I've only been to two.

The first one was two summers ago, I think, and just about the whole school got asked. All I remember about it was that we had the party tea, with all sorts of jellies and cakes and cream things and paper hats and party streamers, out of doors in their garden which was as big as a park, it felt as big as Kew Gardens. We sat at one long table, about a mile long stretching away into the distance, made of trestle-tables put end to end and covered with white cloths so that you couldn't see the joins. And when we'd finished, Isabel-Ann's father stood up at the head of the long table and called out in a loud and jolly voice that we were all to stand and sing one verse of *All People That On Earth Do Dwell*.

It was all very surprising. And pretty special.

But . . . this party the day before yesterday.

It was an indoor party, because it's getting towards winter now, so it wasn't the whole school. Only about twelve people. In fact I was surprised to be asked.

I'm not going to say the name of the person. You'd probably know it, if I said. A lot of the names at our school are the ones you see around town . . . businesses, and so on.

I grew out of my Christmas-time brown velvet ages ago. But my mother got a party dress for me from someone - I don't know who - and it didn't even need altering. It is of shantung silk, with fascinating bumpy bits in the weave, a mysterious rose colour with cinnamon-brown cobwebby-starry patterns here and there.

I think it's lovely.

And the night before, my Mum damped my hair and tied it up in curl-rags, with some of the fine linen strips she saves off the middles of the old sheets, so that we could brush it up into a pretty fuzz at the back.

However, when I got to the party all the girls had special party shoes in little cases, and dresses that looked like bridesmaids or fairy dolls, all frilly and white and foaming like cream. Enough to put you off your tea, to tell you the truth.

And you will hardly believe this . . . they started off with a dress parade! We all had to file round the room while the grown-ups chose the best dresses and awarded prizes to be given out at the end. No prize for mine, I can tell you! The dresses that came top were the frilliest and soppiest of them all.

I just wished I could go home, because after tea it was more competitions. Going round the house with pencil and paper and guessing the names of the advertisements cut from the news-papers and stuck up all over the place. And guessing names of tunes I'd never heard before. I hardly got any right. We only have the wireless on for Children's Hour and the News. And the only papers around the place are *The Times* and *The Daily Telegraph* that Mr Grüning fetches for himself and Miss Elphin.

You will think I'm making it up if I tell you what the prizes were, but it's the truth . . . little metal tubes of *powder* for polish-ing their *finger-nails!* Every prize-winner had the same. The one whose party it was, whispered to me that her father gets them as samples, but I don't know what that means.

But . . . I can't *imagine* anyone wanting to be bothered to polish their *finger-nails*, for goodness sake! Esmé Hickman's was varnish and the time I had that row I was only experimenting. That's different.

When my Mum asked me, I'm afraid I said, "Yes, it was a nice party, thank you!" because she'd only worry if I told her.

But I mentioned it to my Dad when I had the chance. He never lets things like that worry him in the slightest. And I was having such a job trying to work out why people are soppy and silly.

And *are* they silly?

Or is it me that's in a muddle, thinking that they are?

So I asked him. He never answers properly, just makes Comments. All he said was, "Hmph! More-Money-Than-Sense!" But the way he said it made me know he agreed with me and was on my side.

However, that More-Money-Than-Sense thing has left me with a lot more puzzles to work out.

And I can't get to sleep.

* * * *

130

I don't remember lying awake thinking all these thoughts when I was little.

I'd like to go to sleep but I can't let go of this one till I see where it's leading. So here goes:

I can see what my Dad means, because you'd certainly need Money to buy those frilly dresses. And if you had any Sense you wouldn't buy them.

But . . .

What is sillier, having a silly party, or going to a silly school?

The people who had the party are the same ones who send their children to the rich people's silly school, where Granpie sends *me*. I don't actually *know* that he has to pay money to send me, because things like that don't get talked about, but I begin to think it must be that sort of school.

So . . .

What does that make Granpie, who is my Dad's father, and my friend? Does *he* have More-Money-Than-Sense?

This is a very bothersome question.

I've always thought Granpie was about the sensiblest person in the world, as well as the kindest. He always has new ideas for sensible things to do, like showing me how to develop photographs, and make leaf prints on sensitive paper. He's taught me how to use his microscope, and his fretsaw, and his woodworking lathe in the garden shed. These are all things we do over at his and Acton Grannie's house. And they're all sensible. Playing chess and feeding pigeons, too, and lots of other things that have plenty of Sense.

Then . . . Money. He doesn't buy new clothes for himself, ever. And he only smokes one pipe a day. Though he does sometimes buy something for me, like my pavement bicycle that he taught me to ride on the Common.

Only . . .

If Granpie *doesn't* have Money, how can he send me to that school?

And if he *does* have money, why not spend it on something more sensible?

If he had Money, he would find a way for my mother not to work so hard . . . wouldn't he?

I give up. I don't know the answer. But I'm still not sleepy.

*   *   *   *

My mother has £200 in the Post Office Savings Bank. She's had it since before they were married.

That's quite a lot of money but it's not for spending. It's for Saving-For-A-Rainy-Day.

However, there are occasions when she allows herself to give us a little treat out of it. For instance:

I unfortunately have very long narrow feet like my mother. Her big toes got squashed sideways when she was my age from wearing shoes that were the wrong shape or too short. She has awful bunions and she doesn't want that to happen to me. But when I grew out of my last pair we couldn't find any children's shoes in my size. In the end we had to go to Baber's in Regent Street to buy my flat leather lace-ups the colour of an autumn conker, that I polish every night.

And . . . that's where the treat came in. She said, "Let's treat ourselves to tea at Hill's!"

That's round the corner in Oxford Street. It's beautiful and old-fashioned, with tablecloths and silver and dainty china, and a roaring log fire with the flames dancing and winking on all the shiny things. And hot buttered tea-cakes with strawberry jam. And waitresses in black with black shoes and stockings and frilly aprons and caps like Rose Moody . . .

Oh bother and dash and blow, now I'm going to have to get up and go downstairs because I Want-To-Be-Excused . . .

It's so long since I slept up here, I'd forgotten about the two flights down. When I was in the Linen Cupboard, if I had to Get-Up-In-The-Night it was right next door.

Now, I've got to creep down and not step on any creaky stairs to wake people up. Especially not to wake my Mum and Dad up.

When I was little perhaps I didn't have to get up so much. I expect I went straight to sleep instead of lying awake thinking. I don't know. But I don't remember having to do all this creeping.

It's a funny feeling in the middle of the night going past all the rooms . . . across the landing where Mr Sprigget and Mr Grüning and Miss Elphin are all sleeping . . . and secret, behind closed doors . . . and not a sound in the whole house.

I managed to step over where there's a creaky stair on the way down to Miss Fazackerly's room, so I didn't make a sound and

I'm past her door now and into the dark passage along to the Upstairs Lavatory. And I've got my torch with me so I'll be all right and I've only got to get finished and back up the stairs again and into my room . . .

And then I'll be able to go to sleep . . .

Oh what am I to do?

What am I to do?

I'm back in bed and I'm so scared. I know something is terribly wrong. I'm freezing cold and so scared and holding myself tight to stop from shaking, and I'm hoping and hoping and *hoping* that everything's all right, but I know it isn't.

Oh, *what* am I to do?

There's nothing else I *can* do. I've tried and tried and done everything I could.

If I could go to sleep perhaps I'd wake up in the morning and find it was all a bad dream. But I can't.

I can't stop thinking about what has just happened . . . it's going round and round my head.

When I came back along the dark passage again I was shining my torch on the ground to see the steps down. There was a small sound and something white moved and I nearly jumped out of my skin thinking it was a ghost. I wish it had been.

It was Miss Fazackerly in a long white nightie and her hair in pigtails like a little girl. She was standing outside her room with her hands clasped in front of her. I wanted to go past but she gasped in a tiny voice, "Please go and tell your mother that I . . . I . . . that I *can't pass water!*"

I nearly died, but I sort of nodded my head and she went back into her room and closed the door and I tiptoed up the stairs three stairs at a time as fast as I could, until I got to the top landing. And then it was as if my feet were glued to the floor, and I was standing shaking all over and looking at the three steps up to the closed door of my mother-and-father's room.

Never in my life have I seen Miss Fazackerly in anything but her proper clothes. Never in my life have I heard anyone use *those words* . . . I couldn't even *imagine* anyone saying them. But

133

I have to say them.

And I have to knock on this door.

But that is something that you just *do not do!* You don't knock on people's doors in the middle of the night and wake them up. Especially not my mother-and-father's.

In the end, I did. I went up the three steps and lifted my hand to knock, and couldn't do it, and came down to the landing and stood for a bit longer, shaking and shivering and sort of crying inside. I was too scared to cry.

Then I managed it, and knocked. I heard my Dad thump out of bed, because he's the side nearest the door, and he pulled the door open, all tousle-haired and strange, and said crossly, "What is it? What d'you want?"

I said, "It's Miss Fazackerly!" and he said, "What about Miss Fazackerly?" and I said, "She said to tell my mother that she . . . she can't Be-Excused . . . she can't *go to the lavatory!*"

My father said crossly again, "Well, that's nothing to get worked up about, lots of people can't go to the lavatory, it'll come right in its own good time. *Go to bed!*"

So I did.

I wish I could have cried, before I knocked at the door. I did *try* to say those words, but they wouldn't go past my teeth. If only I hadn't been so scared. If only I could have cried, and worked myself up to it.

Then I might have been able to blurt the words out.

I was late waking.

I didn't wake till I heard my mother's call floating up to my window from the side door, "Get up! It's la-ate!"

I scrambled into my clothes, had half a wash, and down to the Kitchen where my mother and father were at the table. She'd finished Mr Grüning's cooked breakfast. Miss Fazackerly's cereal-and-toast breakfast comes later.

I took a big breath to make myself get the words out, and said, "*Is Miss Fazackerly all right?*"

My mother shot me a startled look, put down her spoon and made for the door, saying, "Don't be late for school!" and I gulped some milk and toast and marmalade and was gone before she came back.

After school I ran most of the way home, and into the Kitchen.

I didn't have to ask the question, just looked at my mother. She nodded her head twice, and said, "She died."

I felt afraid, and started trembling, but my Mum said, "Come here to me!"

I ran and buried my face in her and wrapped my arms round her. But she made me look at her, and asked gently, "Tell me what happened, and what Miss Fazackerly said to you. Will you do that?"

So I told her. She murmured to herself, "We'll never know the rights and wrongs of it!" But then she clasped me tight and spoke over the top of my head, very firmly, and sometimes in a strange fierce voice. Like this:

"*Listen* to me, my darling! She was an old lady, older than we guessed and she was very ill and I never realised. She was very brave, and good at hiding pain. Remember her like that, and think of her with God. *You are not to go on blaming yourself!* Now, you just remember that and put it out of your mind, d'you understand?"

By this time we were both crying and hugging each other. But my Mum pushed me away from her and smiled at me through the tears till in the end she had us laughing at the mess we were both in. Then she gave me a friendly smack on the bottom, and said:

"There now, that's enough! She was a brave lady. Just remember that and be glad of it and forget all the rest. The thing to do is carry on as usual . . . now, run along and change and go out to play till tea-time."

So, if I don't mention Miss Fazackerly again, please don't think I've forgotten her. I'm just doing as my mother said.

135

17

EVERYTHING GETS MADE NEW

It's coming on towards Christmas and . . . oh, this is just the best time of the whole year in the Kitchen. There are so many marvellous things to be made in advance . . . the cakes and Christmas puddings and mincemeat and everything . . . the place seems to be full of gorgeous Christmassy smells for days and days.

The place is all lemony and orangey and spicey. And I'm doing my special Christmas ingredients-getting-ready jobs which I wouldn't mind going on doing all day, instead of going over to Granpie's later on, the way I always do on a Saturday.

Though I love being at Granpie's, too.

I wish I could be in two places at once.

Anyway, my mother is weighing out flour, sugar, sultanas and currants, making breadcrumbs, grating nutmeg, measuring mixed spice, beating eggs, and lots of other things like doing the lunch at the same time.

And I'm sitting at the kitchen table doing my favourite jobs, which are:

1. Stoning the raisins. They are big, juicy, flavoury raisins and are full of grape pips that you have to feel around for and get out with your fingers, before you can use them in a pudding or whatever. They come in a shiny blue paper poke, and are all squashy and have a delicious taste.
2. Blanching almonds, only I call it popping the almonds, because you have to pop them out of their skins. You put them to soak for a while in a bowl of very hot water and test them to see when the skins are soft enough. Then you take out a few at a time, hold each one between finger and thumb and . . . pop! . . . out jumps the shiny white almond and you're left with the empty brown skin. You have to watch out not to jump too many of them onto the floor.
3. Grating the suet, which comes from the butcher's in a big lump. It's not the actual grating of it that is fun, but disentangling the skin. It has a very thin, transparent, filmy skin that separates the lump into different-sized sections. Once it's all separated out and no skin left, you grate it on the grater, which is just an ordinary job. But the suet has a lovely clean, waxy feel and is nice to work with.
4. Getting the Candied Peel ready for my mother to chop up. This is more of a treat than a job, and is the most Christmassy one of all. When you open the tucked-in top of the paper poke and tip the pieces out onto the table, you never know quite what you'll find, nor how much candied sugar there'll be in each one.

   You know when you cut an orange in half, and eat the inside and leave the peel whole? That's what it is - whole halves of orange and lemon or sometimes even grapefruit peel. They've been candied in sugar, and the left-over sugar has gone solid in the bottom of each one, like ice in a pool. It's hard, like a sugar mouse, but with a magic tangy taste.

   The sugar's no good for anything, so you bend the peel back till the sugar pops out, and then eat it.

So there you are! Along with cutting up the salt, those are defi-

137

nitely my most favourite Kitchen things to do.

The happy Christmassy feeling makes them extra special, too. My Mum is humming while she spoons the flour out of the sweetie-jar, and adds things and mixes and beats. She looks up with a smile from time to time and says things like, "It'll be time to make the paper-chains before we know where we are!" or, "It's nice that there are so many holly berries this year!"

I should have explained that the holly tree is in our front garden. It has grown tall and thin from being so close to the house, just to the left of the front door as you go out. All the berries are at the top, level with Mr Grüning's right-hand window. So it's not too difficult to reach out with the secateurs and cut pieces from there, and cut some more from the other side of the tree by going out onto the little balcony of the Dressing Room.

The Dressing Room is up above the front porch, and belongs to Mr Sprigget's Blue Room. But it also has its own separate door onto the landing. Provided we ask Mr Sprigget first, we can go straight through the Dressing Room and out onto the balcony and take our time choosing the best berry branches, without spoiling the tree.

So there are plenty of Christmas jobs to do at home, as well as school stuff like practising for the dancing display and finishing off the things we're making for presents. This year it's felt egg cosies and raffia napkin rings and a tapestry picture of a thatched cottage.

I've finished the tapestry though, thank goodness.

And there's only a bit more to do on the special secret cushion-cover for my mother which I hope she's going to like very much. It's daffodils and crocuses done with embroidery wools of the most beautiful, true, lifelike colours. Three different yellows, a purple, and four lovely shades of deep green for the backs and fronts of the leaves, all growing and blowing as if they're in a woodland place.

And there's still homework to do.

I got a row about it at school last week.

To tell you the truth, it's quite difficult finding time for everything these days.

How it happened was, I swapped Guide Companies about a

month ago. Instead of the silly school Company, I'm in Pauline's one.

Well, our Headmistress stands at the top of the stairs every morning to catch you on your way up from Prayers, if she wants to Have-A-Word. I've had a row before, but only for eating sweets in the street (which is against the rules) on the way back from Netball. But this is the first time she's ever had to Have-A-Word with me about my work, so it wasn't very nice. You get so used to being good and law-abiding that it comes as a shock to be told, "Stop neglecting your school work or you'll have to give up Guides!"

Help!

You can bet I'm not going to let that happen!

Because Pauline was right. Her Company, that I'm in now, does all the things she said, like signalling and camping and going on hikes and cooking sausages and dampers on fires that really work. I even enjoy marching and drill. And they're serious about things that are important, like the Promises and the Guide Law.

But the best part of it is that they're not sloppy and silly. The Captain and the Lieutenant and all the older Guides like my Patrol Leader and Second are expert at things, and expect everyone else to become just as good. So if you're doing a test, you only pass it if you know your stuff and do it nearly perfectly.

I like that.

It's the Morse Code I'm learning at the moment, for my Second Class Badge, and then you have to practise sending and receiving. It's hard, but really exciting, and a whole lot more useful and interesting than school.

We don't do much singing at school, either, but we do at Guides because it's one of this Company's special things. As it's winter, we do it indoors and sit in a circle round a pretend camp-fire. Every week, there's something new to learn, things I never knew existed. Not just new songs, but new ways of singing. Like Rounds, and singing in two parts, and also in canon, which is beautiful . . . the sounds floating up and down, and mixing and mingling.

But I have to be careful.

It's easy to do something so stupid, you wish the ground would swallow you up.

Especially when you're new. And the others know all the songs and you've got to pick them up as you go along. And you think you've heard the words right, so you sing along in a very grown-up and know-everything way. Like when I sang:

"Where is John? The cows are in the corn again!

Oh, Where is John, the old Lieutenant's leftopin?"

and was wondering all the time what on earth a 'leftopin' was, and what the Lieutenant wanted with one, and anyway, why were they calling the Lieutenant 'old', when she's really quite young and pretty?

I puzzled about it a lot, till I found out next week that they were actually singing:

"Oh, where is John? The old red hen has left her pen!"

So things are confusing, sometimes.

I was glad it was a Round, so probably no one heard me, anyway.

If I am to be truthful, what I like best are the very quiet songs. There's one called Deep Peace, which ends:

'Deep peace of the shining stars to you,

Deep peace of the Son of Peace to you!'

and before that it's about the running waves and the flowing air, and we sing it so softly that it's like the earth breathing.

Also, after every meeting, just before we go home, we sing 'Taps'. This is how it goes. Only you have to imagine the quietness, and the sort of spacey, listening feel that there is to it . . .

'Day is do - ne . . .

Gone the su - n . . .

From the hills, from the sea, from the sky,

All . . . is . . . we - ll . . .

Sa - fely rest . . .

Go - d . . . is nigh!'

Talking about that reminds me of last night.

Although it's the end of November, and a frosty feel to the air, there are still a few Cox's Orange quite high up on the apple trees. There's nothing as crunchy-cold and delicious as a Cox's that you pick in the wintry stillness, after school with just enough light left to see by.

I'm allowed to use the long-handled pruner. It's about seven foot long, not heavy, so I can reach well up the tree if I stretch. The trick is to wiggle the curved cutting-blade round the stalk, pull the handle . . . snick! . . . and at the same time drop the pruner quick as lightning and try to catch the apple before it hits the ground.

I could see the apples up there, about nine left, just dark shapes. All the leaves were gone, and the twigs and apples made a dark pattern against the evening sky. My apple fell fast and I missed my catch but it didn't matter. I spotted where it landed, gave it a rub and had a good bite, all sharp-and-sweet and frosty-smelling.

Then I stood still, just looking.

The sky was deep blue up above but shading down paler like the shallows of the sea. Nothing moved. Quietness over everything. The long strands and little flecks of clouds low in the west were sand-gold shores and islands . . . so real, not flat but stretching away and away and away to far distances, and a greeny-blue sea between . . . pale duck-egg-green water, going away out between the islands to a far horizon, and a light shining through it . . . calling me . . . calling me . . .

What is it?

Why is this gladness bursting inside me and yet I want to cry?

Then I saw the first star, very pure and white in the green sea. It somehow calmed the golden islands down and rested the pulling of the far horizons.

And yet . . . it's so strange . . . for a minute I couldn't look away. It was as if the star saw me, and I saw the star, we were looking at each other . . . and I held my breath while that little speck of brightness gathered all the meaning of the sky into itself, and said something to me.

Then it let go, and I started breathing again.

It left me with a great feeling of peace, though I didn't know why. And a feeling of wonder, at that bright world hanging there so steadily and quietly, with Space all around. The same feeling that is in the words of the hymn that says:

> 'Out beyond the shi - ning of the farthest star
> Thou art always stre - tching infinitely far,'

which is one that I like very much, and I started humming it and put the pruner away and went on munching my frosty apple.

My Dad is interested in stars and has shown me the Great Bear, Cassiopeia, the Seven Sisters, and our greatest favourite, which is Orion with his Dog Star. I think my one probably wasn't a star but a planet, which he's told me about, too. But I forget whether it's Venus or Mercury that you see in the evening.

It's amazing to think that we're one, as well. A planet, I mean. Hanging up there like that. Except that *it* is up, and we are down. But if we were on Mercury or whatever, we'd say, "That's Earth up there!" So 'up' and 'down' don't mean anything, really. Not when you're talking about us being in Space.

Another thing I was thinking is, a star is like something that is old and new at the same time. When a star comes out, it's new. One moment there's a sea-green sky-ocean and . . . in the blink of an eye, the next second a star appears as if it has just been born. Yet it's millions and millions of years old.

When I finished in the garden and went in to get some bread and syrup, I was thinking about Peter Pan and hoping we would go to see it again this year.

Granpie often takes us as a Christmas treat and I never seem to grow out of enjoying it. There's such a magic feel to it, with the stars, and 'straight on till morning'. You can really believe in them flying, and believe in the battle with the pirates and Captain Hook, too. I love the bit where the stage is split into two levels so that you can see both at once . . . the pirates searching in the wood up the top . . . and the underground house down below, with the Lost Boys safe asleep in the big bed. And always Peter Pan flying.

I'll tell you another thing that's special about it.

Every year it's the same play.

But every year it's different!

That's pretty strange, when you think about it . . . things being old and yet new, and the same but different.

I like that.

*   *   *   *

I was thinking, I suppose a boarding-house is like that.

Not just ours, but any boarding-house.

Still the same house, and still the same us, but people come and go.

A bit like a river.

We go to Kew Gardens sometimes. Not very often, just once in a blue moon. But it's my mother's favourite place to go if we get the chance. My Dad likes it too, especially along the towing path where we can see the herons standing along the Syon House reach, and you can see the river running strongly.

The water in the river flows fast, so it must be going somewhere. Out to sea, I suppose.

It's still the same River Thames.

But it's getting made new all the time.

Except sometimes the river runs quickly, and sometimes slowly. And that's the way it is with us.

There's a new lady, a Miss Hooper, in Devonshire Grannie's Room, but otherwise we're much the same at the moment. Miss Hooper is very nice, quite quiet and friendly, but we don't see a lot of her, as she goes Up-To-Town every day on the train to her office and often doesn't come home till late. She wears neat but smart clothes, and when she goes out in the morning a nice little waft of scenty-perfumey air follows her down the Stately Stairs and along the Front Hall, the way it used to in Mr Dupré's time.

And that's about all I can tell you.

I'm still in the Room Next to the Tank Cupboard - no one else new there yet. Mrs Ritchie has settled in nicely and is getting quite excited about her first Christmas with us. She's good at keeping Miss Elphin cheered up, and also gives Mr Grüning the odd chuckle. And Mr Sprigget is a peaceful fellow, brisk and busy with his business and keeps himself to himself as usual.

So that's the way it is.

Some people come and go quickly, like when the river is running very fast, and you drop a stick into the water and it swirls away and out of sight almost too quickly to keep your eye on.

And some people are with us for a long time, like when the river runs into a backwater and almost stops flowing, and it collects bits and pieces of leaves and sticks, the way people collect little things to decorate their rooms if they're going to be staying a good while.

It's true, what I said about being so used to guests coming and going that you don't think twice about it.

But it's also true that if they've been here quite a long time, you miss them when they're gone.

There are other ones, like Miss Mole, who are supposed to come back, and don't.

We've been keeping her cabin trunk, that has nothing in it but dozens of her blue exercise books full of writing, for I don't know how long, because she asked my mother and father to keep them till she came again. At least, I think that's why. Though I can't be sure.

Anyway, it's getting nearer and nearer to Christmas. When it's nearly Christmas Eve and we can't bear waiting any longer, my Dad will go down to the shops one morning for a few mysterious things and come back with a tall Christmas-tree on his shoulder, ready to set up in the Lounge.

So this Saturday he said, "D'you want to come and hunt up the decorations?" and we went up together to the Tank Cupboard to climb over everything and find the proper box.

When he turned the key and opened the door onto that blackness, before he switched on the light, just for a second there was a scritchy-scratchy scrabbling and a quick scurry. And there was a trail of little scraps of paper on the floor, leading to a hole in the bottom corner of Miss Mole's trunk.

My Dad didn't say anything, because he very seldom does. He just went, "Hmph!" threw open the lid and quickly turned back the top layer of exercise books. You could see straight away where the pages had been chewed up, down in that bottom corner, and made into a sort of nest, but the mice had run off. My Dad didn't say so, but he'll be putting down traps, that's obvious, and probably in my room next door as well, because they get behind the skirting.

Anyway, he was looking a bit grim, and fed up, and he flopped the top layer of books back so that he could shut the lid. But before he shut it, he lifted a book from the top of the pile, and looked at it. It had a title in inverted commas, written in capitals on the cover, and the title was the name of our house.

I'm beginning to think I don't want to say any more of this.

Because I didn't like it, and nor did he.

And you might find it hard to believe . . . but it's the truth.

My Dad opened the exercise book at the first page. The first sentence was short. It was on a line by itself, and it said:

'This is a house without a soul.'

My Dad snapped the book shut and made a sharp sound, half way between a sob and a snort. Then he dropped the lid and shoved the trunk to one side, saying, "*That lot will have to go!*" and I climbed over the junk and found the box of decorations and a few other bits and pieces, and we shut the door and never spoke about it again.

By the time there was a moment to think about it, I'd stopped feeling upset, and was feeling angry.

A house can't have a soul, for goodness sake! So what Miss Mole was really saying was that *we* didn't have one . . . that my father and mother haven't got a soul. That's enough to make *anyone* angry.

But very soon I wanted to laugh, just because she was so wrong. And I can forgive her, and have a laugh about it, because she didn't understand.

I *know* how wrong she was.

But I'm not going to explain why.

At least, not exactly.

If you didn't know my father well, you'd think he was a person with very few feelings, because the only time he shows any is if he's pestered and gets annoyed. However, he has very deep feelings hidden away inside him. They don't show at all, except when he's singing. Even then, you can't be sure, because when he sings he becomes the person who is speaking to you in the song.

Sometimes it is as if the person in the song is just talking, or speaking very low, or crying out, or even shouting. He suits his voice to the song, and suits his feelings to the song. Sometimes they can be very powerful, and you know he is feeling them himself and not just pretending.

145

When my mother sings, it is different, because she is always herself. She doesn't suit her feelings to the song, but suits the song to her feelings . . . chooses the sort of music that matches how she feels.

If she's light-hearted, and has a moment to spare for a bit of music, it might be one of her concert songs, or perhaps *Caller Herrin'*, which goes ripplingly in long runs of light notes like the silver herrings pouring out of the nets.

And when she dreadfully needs to say something that you can't say with words, and wants to put all her heart into it and sing with the full beautiful power of her voice, then it has to be one of her grand ones that end up fortissimo.

But today was different.

It's Sunday today, the day after my Dad and I went up to the Tank Cupboard for the decorations.

Sunday dinner is finished and cleared and washed up, so I was going to go back into the Dining Room and get on with making the paper-chains. We bought the packets of coloured paper strips from Woolworth's last week, and the big dining table is the best place to do it, with plenty of room to spread the chain out as it grows longer and longer.

When I got to the door I heard the piano.

I'd thought my mother would have been having a Sunday rest, but she was in the Dining Room just starting to play something very quietly.

At first I didn't know what it was.

But then I did. It was the end of *The Lost Chord*, but all the time quietly, even where it's meant to be fortissimo. She was just singing very softly, as if she was thinking the words to herself, and not meaning anyone else to hear. So I kept outside the door and didn't let on that I was there, while she sang, so low and soft, but happily:

> "It link'd all perplexed meanings . . .
> Into one perfect peace,
> And trembled away into silence . . .
> As if it were loth to cease;
> I have sought, but I seek it vainly . . .

146

That one lost chord divine,
Which came from the soul of the organ . . .
And entered into mine.
It may be that Death's bright Angel . . .
Will speak in that chord again;
It may be that only in Heav'n . . .
I shall hear that grand Amen . . . "

And she sang the last part over again, slowly and thoughtfully, and kept going to the end of the accompaniment.

But then it finished, and there was a silence. And then the slap of music sheets being changed and she started on *The Holy City*, which is one of her favourites for letting rip on. So I went in and sat at the table and listened, and began spreading out the paper-chain strips and sorting the colours. And my Mum smiled across at me and kept going.

Sometimes when she lets rip it's because it's All-Too-Much, and she's all tightened up inside and needs to let the lid off.

And sometimes she does it, I think, because she's sad and unhappy, but she plays herself out of it and becomes glad and glorious by the end.

But this time she was singing as if there was a quiet joyfulness in her that she had to sing about, like a blackbird at evening, full of contented gladness. Especially when she came to the last verse, that goes:

"And once again the scene was changed,
New earth there seemed to be,
I saw the Holy City beside the tideless sea,
The light of God was on its streets,
The gates were opened wide,
And all who would might enter,
And no one was denied . . . "

And then her voice soared into the last chorus in grand glorious-ness, as if she was telling the whole world, saying and saying, with all her heart and all her mind and all her strength and all her soul, that everything will be all right for ever and ever:

"Jeru - salem! Jeru - salem!
Sing . . . for the night is o'er!

147

Ho - sanna . . . in the Hi - ghest,
Hosanna for ever more!"

She finished, put the music rest down and shut the lid, and came over and sank back into the low armchair that sits by the Cosy-Stove in the winter, when the piano has been shifted. It's an old furry-green nursing chair, low and wide, and the best one for curling up in to read a book. It's also the best one for having a cuddle in, the way I still like to do just once in a while.

So I asked, "Can I have a cuddle?" and slid onto her lap and nestled into her shoulder, which is a very nice feeling, and we didn't say anything for a bit.

Then I said, thinking out loud, "I'll be twelve next year!"

She hugged me and said, "I know! You great big lass! Much too big for cuddles, but . . . all those years! It seems no time at all since we came here in '27 when you were born!"

I hadn't really thought about it before. Well, you can't imagine life being anything except what it is, but . . . she could have been a singer, and . . . all those years, cooking and washing and looking after us all . . .

So I said, in a small voice, "Isn't it very hard?"

My Mum thought for a bit, and then said very cheerfully, "Yes! I suppose it is! But it's part of life, and I'll tell you this . . . *I am not sorry for one little bit of it!*"

She gave me a friendly slap and pushed me off her knee saying, "Come on, I must make a sponge for their tea . . . and you'd better get those new paper-chains finished before Christmas catches up with you!"

PART TWO

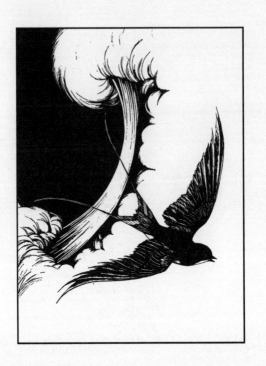

1

THE AMAZING PLACE

Granpie is always watching for me coming on a Saturday.

It's like having Christmas every week.

I get off the trolley-bus at Acton and run through the straight streets of little houses all joined together and all looking the same, and arrive at Granpie's which is no different on the outside but very different on the inside, and there he is, standing at the bow-window.

He doesn't smile or wave but only disappears. I know that Acton Grannie will be sitting by the stove in that room, which is the Dining Room, and that Granpie is hurrying out to the hall to let me in. I reach the front door just as he opens it, and when he closes it behind me the street has changed to wavery shapes of red and green and gold through the glass, and I feel excited because it is Saturday. I put my arms round Granpie's neck and give him a hug. He is not much taller than me and I kiss him on his bristly whiskers.

Every Saturday it is the same. He says, "Be a good girl and hang your coat up and let's see what the fairies have brought!"

And I run down the passage to the Drawing Room, with him hurrying after as fast as he can.

He hurries because he is just as excited as I am, and just as happy when we find the tiny parcel and unwrap it. He says, "Well, bless my soul! It's a . . . " whatever it is. And I say, "Oh, Granpie, it's beautiful!" because it always is. I'll tell you more about it later, and also why the Drawing Room should really be called the Amazing Place. But there are things I ought to explain first.

Granpie and I both know that it is he who brings the presents, and not the fairies, but we don't spoil it for each other by saying so.

Another thing is that now I am eleven, in fact nearly twelve, we don't actually mention fairies any more. Things still sometimes appear but they are more likely to be useful objects such as, say, a globe pencil sharpener that comes apart at the Equator to let the shavings out. And we don't pretend about it, so I can thank him properly which I am very glad to do, because I like these things and they are just as special. It always has been special going over to Granpie's and it still is, in lots of ways that I haven't even begun to explain yet, only there is something I had better own up to first.

This 'Be a good girl' saying, that I said just now, is true. But there ought to be a gap between 'hang your coat up' and 'let's see what the fairies have brought'.

The reason I stuck them together like a sandwich was so that you would know the exciting feeling I always get when I arrive. When I was little I sometimes nagged to look in the Drawing Room first, but only when I was being what my Dad calls a Pestilential Nuisance, because of course the thing to do is to go straight away and say hallo to Acton Grannie in the Dining Room.

The Dining Room is a small square room with a bow-window onto the street, and is mostly taken up with the big square table where we paint and draw and write and play dominoes and chess and do huge jigsaw puzzles and lots of other things, as well as have meals. It must be awful being blind like Acton Grannie, as well as old and big and heavy and not all that good at walking, and she spends most of the time sitting by the stove on the other side of the table, knitting things on thick wooden needles about a foot-and-a-half long. She can feel with her fingers when she drops a stitch but she can't pick it up, so after I have given her a kiss and she has asked me about school, she shows me her knitting and I try to put it right. Often it's a lot of rows down and takes ages, but then I am finished and it is time for the Amazing Place.

Acton Grannie says, "Now you run along then!" And I run out of the Dining Room which has dark green wallpaper and dark brown paint, and into the hall and the long straight passage that is even darker brown, as dark as a burrow.

I run down the passage with Granpie hurrying after as fast at he can, past the wonderful smells of Saturday roast coming from the kitchen door on the left where Mrs Liddington is cooking it, till we get to what you would think is a dead end, only it isn't a dead end but the door to the Drawing Room.

Granpie is at my shoulder and I open the door and suddenly we are out of the dark and into the light. It is all light and white and gold and mirrors and windows, with sunshine and greenery outside. At first you can hardly see for the brightness because the end wall is all French windows into the garden, the paper is all white with gold and grey stripes and pretty patterns and a mirror over the white fireplace.

And then.

Oh my!

You still wonder where the brightness is coming from and you turn round to look at the wall you've just come in at, and it's as if there's no wall there at all, but maybe another window or an opening into heaven or something. Almost the whole wall is mirror, a most beautiful mirror framed in gold. It is straight at the bottom and the sides but curved and curly at the top and going up into a dome shape. On what is left of the wall either side of the dome-shaped top, hang golden carved niches with gold pillars and gold pointed fretty roofs and in each stands a strong angel in red and blue clothes, facing inwards and blowing a long golden trumpet so that the whole room goes up with a shout.

The sunlight from the garden flashes from the glass.

Granpie stops for a moment as if he is taking a breath, then lets it out in a little sigh and mutters something into his beard.

He doesn't say anything.

Then he clasps his hands behind his back, tucks his head forwards from his hunchy shoulders, and goes with his short, happy, hurrying steps towards the big round table in the corner by the

153

French windows, doing his whispery siffling whistling under his breath. This time it's not *Guide-Me-O-Thou* but *Jerusalem the Golden*.

I don't think he knows he is doing it.

I like it. It means he is happy.

We hurry up and open the little paper bag. It's just lying on the table, not hidden, because we have far too many interesting things to do, to be bothered wasting time 'getting hot' and 'getting cold'.

On the table is a pale green cloth with fringes. On the cloth is the dolls' house that Granpie made me years ago, with a sliding front so as not to knock the garden over, with four rooms and a hall and landing, proper front and back doors and electric light from a battery. Granpie and I finished furnishing it ages ago from the things the fairies brought, but just now and again something special takes his fancy and gets added.

Inside the little bag are two lumpy somethings in tissue paper. We unwrap it carefully and set the things on the table . . . a tiny brass kettle, so small it could sit on a threepenny bit, with a separate little brass trestle-stand for it to balance on.

"Well, bless my soul!" says Granpie. "It's exactly like our one!" He tries to lift the lid, but his big square fingers won't go under the handle, so I do it, and say, "Look, you can even put water in and pour it out! It's lovely!"

I slide the front off the dolls' house and put the kettle on the dresser. The sun shines on it and makes me wish I could go out into the garden. I'm getting a bit old for playing, now that my brain is just about full up with Morse and Semaphore and knots and Guide Laws and things. But I don't want to hurt Granpie's feelings, and anyway I've always loved the dolls' house.

Not dolls! Ugh! Dolls are horribly awfully boring. And . . . taking their clothes on and off, and putting them to bed! What could be worse! I'd rather sit and paint, any day. Wrightie gave me a beautiful big doll once, but I never played with it and didn't keep it. At home we only have Baloo (our big old ragged teddy bear with a grunt and a plum-stained tummy) and Uncle James's Rabbit, who have been part of the family always.

There is a family of dolls in the dolls' house. They are about two-and-a-half inches high, with expressionless china faces, and

are the only dull things in it. But you can plonk them on chairs and forget them. The rest of it is totally fascinating, with minia-ture books in the bookcase, miniature plaster fruit in a bowl, a tiny sponge and soap and loofah in the bath rack and little pictures on the walls. A lot of those things Granpie and I made ourselves, as well as the bedding and curtains, and he let me choose the paper for each room out of an old wallpaper book. But there were still plenty of things that we had to leave to the fairies, like the saucepans and flat irons, carpet sweeper and dustpan and brush, and a wonderful little cooker with an adjustable plate-rack and an oven door that opens.

So I expect it will be quite a long time before I get too old for it. There's such a lot of arranging and rearranging you can do, shifting the furniture round and so on, that once I start on it I forget all the other things I thought were more important.

"I'll leave you to it, shall I?" says Granpie, and makes for the door. But then he comes back, which I know he wanted to do anyway, but he had to think of a reason.

"Might as well check the lights while I'm at it," he mutters, and disappears round the back to fiddle with the battery, and I check the switches. There's a separate one in each room and they are the only things out of scale, even though they are the smallest you can buy, about the size of a penny.

"There's a wiggly screw in the bedroom switch, Granpie," I say, checking the pink bulb with the rosy glow, "and the bathroom bulb's gone phut!"

"Never mind!" he says happily, coming round to the front. "We'll buy new ones next time we're in Woollies'. Where's that screw?" And he takes his smallest screwdriver from his waistcoat pocket and gets busy, humming now instead of whistle-breathing.

This time it's *Gaudeamus igitur* and I join in, because he taught it to me ages ago, so we sing the words out loud a few times until we get tired of it. It goes:

> Gaudeamus igitur
> Juvenes dum sumus.

That's one of the songs he remembers from when he was at college, which was an awfully long time ago. And the other one is:

155

We won't be home till morning,
We won't be home till morning,
We won't be home till mor - or - ning . . .
And so say all of us!

Which is what he used to sing to me when he was pushing me in
my push-chair and we were late getting back from somewhere.

The 'Gaudeamus' one means 'Let us therefore rejoice, because
we are young', and feels a bit more grown-up, perhaps on account
of it being Latin.

Even so, it's when he is feeling about the same age as me, that
Granpie hums it.

Why does he only whistle-breathe hymns, but hums songs?
That's funny, when you think about it.

Come to think of it, a lot of things are funny.

Well . . . puzzling, anyway.

One is, it's not only that he feels about the same age as me, but
that I feel he is, too. He looks old, of course, but most of the time
he feels more like my age than the people who actually are, such
as Nadine Strachey in my class, who does tap-dancing and sings
all the new songs like that *Poop-poop-dinna-donna-wanna* one
she was doing for us this week.

Anyway, I don't think of Granpie as old, whereas Acton
Grannie is like a . . . well, I'm sorry for Acton Grannie and
perhaps I shouldn't think this way, but . . . she truly is like an old,
old rock on a hillside, with her long thick black skirts down to the
ground to keep the draughts off, and the fawn braid on them and
her fawn shawl like very old moss that's been growing for years.

But when I think about it, Granpie must really be very old, too.
I know when he was born because he told me.

1860! Can you imagine?

He feels the same age as me . . . and yet he was 67 when I was
only being born!

That reminds me . . .

The angels on the wall come from when Granpie was in Italy,
long ago before I was born. Probably before my Dad and Aunt
Marjorie were born, or even before he married Acton Grannie.
What a strange thought! I wonder how he carried the golden

niches back, because they are quite large and complicated, with sticking-out bits. People must have had very large suitcases in those days.

This is also the Amazing Place because you never know what treasures you are going to unearth.

Nobody uses this room to live in so it's a good place to store toys and games, and there's a load of them stacked away behind the sofa. As well as Meccano and Ludo, and tin toys that wind up and walk along beating drums or pushing prams or whatever, there are also four special things, which are:

1. Granpie's Magic Lantern, that he sets up and shows funny films on the wall with, and all the exciting long thin boxes with the slides in, long slides with round pictures of Mickey Mouse and Donald Duck.

2. My castle, made of rough brown stuff that feels like stone, with proper battlements and a drawbridge that lets down on chains, and all the boxes of lead soldiers marching, or playing band instruments, or galloping on horseback with banners flying. I must admit I still sometimes play with them on winter days and set them out all over the floor, the way Granpie and I do the clockwork train set, which is another special thing because of all the little model porters and trolleys to put luggage on, bridges and trees, and best of all the little posters, just like real ones, of Oxo, and the Bisto Kids and Pears Soap and also showing beautiful travel scenes of mountains and waterfalls.

3. A very old box of building bricks, with wonderful pillars and fanlights, and windows with red and green celluloid panes.

4. Auntie Marjorie's toy cooking stove that she had when she was small, made out of grey metal like a proper range with a chimney, and an oven and fire door that open on little brass hinges, and a long-shaped water urn thing with a tiny brass tap that really works.

But . . .
That's not all by a long chalk.

157

The sofa is under the angels' heaven-mirror. The dolls' house table is in the far corner by the French windows, with the upright piano in the other window corner. And on the long wall, beside the piano, is . . . a big , old, black cabin trunk.

Nobody . . . nobody at all, not even me . . . is allowed to open it, except Granpie himself.

Inside, first of all you come to the tray that lifts out, and in it are lying long lengths of wood with proper sleepers and O-gauge railway tracks fixed on them. Two of the sections have proper spring buffers at one end.

The tray has sort of tape handles. Granpie goes to one end with me at the other. We lift very, very carefully, and both together, and lay the tray on the Drawing Room carpet. But only he is allowed to lift the two engines that he made himself, because they're heavy and because they are his Pride and Joy.

You would understand why, if you saw them.

The polished paintwork, the cast iron wheels, the gleaming pistons, the boiler and safety-valve, and the dials and brass levers and handles in the cab, are exact in every detail and . . . ready to go the minute we get steam up, which we can't do here in the Drawing Room because of the wetness of the steam and the smell of methylated spirit. It's handy to keep them here, though, ready to carry out into the garden.

So I won't say any more about them till later.

And I'd better hurry up and tell you about the last of the treasures in here, before it's time for lunch.

They live on the whatnot in the far corner beyond the heaven-mirror and are from Italy like the angels. There's a model gondola about a foot long, which has a very special feel to it, as if it is made like the real Venetian ones. It's light to hold, of thin wood or maybe papery stuff, painted a tarry black. And there's the Lion of St. Mark, from Venice also, about the size of Granpie's hand, but very heavy. He's made of bronze and is black-coloured and very strong and alive, with his tail waving and one paw on the open pages of his Gospel.

But the best treasure is the one that doesn't look anything much at first, sitting there on the shadowy bottom shelf of the whatnot like a clump of cobweb. Even when it's lifted out, and you see that it's a beautifully carved stone model of St. Peter's in Rome, about nine inches high and hollow inside, with the dome

and dozens of little windows and balconies, you still might not think it was anything special . . . unless it was the holidays and you were staying the night, like me.

When it gets dark we take it into the Dining Room.

Granpie gets a night-light from the chiffonier drawer and puts it on a plate on the table, and lights it and puts St. Peter's down on top and I switch off the light at the door and . . .

The whole of it glows . . . the stone is carved so thin that the soft light shines all pearly through the dome, as well as like stars at every little window. Grannie puts her hands on the dome to feel it, and then goes back to her chair.

And Granpie and I sit and gaze and gaze until it seems that we are small and it is big, and we could walk right in the door and hear the music.

"Can I have a swing before dinner-time, Granpie?" I ask, because I have finished with the dolls' house and put the front back on.

I have to ask, because it is an indoor swing that hangs from the passage ceiling, a few inches from the Drawing Room door, and once I am on it nobody can get past.

" 'May I'," he corrects. "Yes, you may. But be a good girl and wash your hands in plenty of time. It's roast lamb and new potatoes today!"

He goes and unhooks the swing from where it's looped up high on the wall out of the way, and double-checks it to see that it is safe. He made it himself, out of planed wood and thick new rope and huge hooks screwed into a reinforced strip on the ceiling, and the open ends of the hooks tied across with thick black rubber so that the ropes can't jump off when I go high. So it is sure to be safe. But Granpie is very particular and a good workman, and does everything as perfectly as he can.

"There we are, then!" he says and stumps away back to Grannie, and I hop on and face the way he is going, so that I can watch him, and wave when he gets to the Dining Room door.

Swinging is one of the best things there is. Out of doors is better, of course, but even indoors after a bit everything starts to wheel and whirl like Earth turning in Space and you don't know that you are you any more, you're just part of it.

And this swing is very strange and very special, too.

159

Because when I'm facing this way I'm swinging into the dark, but the brightness of the Amazing Place is there all the time behind me, and flashes round my head every time I swing back.

And when I grab the ropes together and stop and jump off and get on the other way round, I'm swinging into the dazzle of sun and greenery and light and white. But when the swing swoops back into the passage I go into the dark and my head and my insides fall into a black hole.

But then I fly back into the light again and I feel like the sparrow in the psalm who has found a home on God's altars.

2

ACTON GRANNIE'S DINING ROOM

There is a comfy feel to the Dining Room, especially on chilly, dark days, with the lamp lit and Grannie's Cosy-Stove, like our one, glowing behind its mica windows, or with the front open ready to roast chestnuts between the bars.

It's small, like a nest or a squirrelly sort of place, and has a settled feeling . . . not like home with all the guests, and people coming and going, and always jobs to do. It's warm and woolly, because of the old brown bobble cloth on the table. And happy, because of all the games and interesting things we get up to after lunch. And there's always a nice lingering smell from roasts and stews and from Granpie's favourite that he calls 'Great Old', which is short for Great Old Apple Pudding, steamed in a basin lined with suet and turned out all collapsed on a dish, and from brown sugar and honey and strawberry jam in a jam-pot in the chiffonier cupboard.

However, the Dining Room is a place that it's as well to walk into, and not run in a hurry, for two reasons.

One is, that Grannie might be coming out. She moves slowly

161

with a shuffling step and her hands out in front to feel the way, so it would be a shock for her to be collided with.

When she was going out of the room once, I asked her what it is like to be always in the dark. She gave a sort of laugh and said, "If only I were!" and went on shuffling, which was scarey.

But then she stopped and held onto the corner of the table, and explained that she always sees coloured lights. "But," she said, heaving a sigh, "the shelves of jam-jars or tins or books, they are the worst . . . I never know when they'll suddenly be there, blocking my way. Oh, I know they're not real, but I still feel I'm going to bump into them! I can tell you that's not very nice, my child!"

Well, it isn't! It must be awful. So that's why I've always remembered, since then, to be careful. Imaginary objects are bad enough without having real ones crash into you.

The other reason why it's not such a good idea to run into the Dining Room in a hurry is that even apart from banging into Acton Grannie, you'd probably bang into the chiffonier. It's on the right-hand wall just as you come into the room, and there isn't all that much space between it and the table.

However, I think I'll explain the Dining Room by going round the other way, to the left, although it's just as much of a squeeze.

You have to shut the door first, to get round. Behind it, you come to Granpie's and my small billiard table leaning against the wall in its fawn cotton dust-cover, with the marker board hanging up above it, and the cues propped up, ready for when we lift it up onto the table. And that's the end of that wall.

Next you come to the bow-window looking out onto the street. In front of it is Granpie's little work table with two small drawers full of hammer and screwdrivers, gimlet, pincers and pliers, nails and tacks and screws, drawing-pins, sealing-wax, fuse-wire, rolled-up bits of string, pencils, pipe-cleaners, old squeezed-up tubes of glue with pins stuck in the top to keep the glue from coming out, and a very special and wonderful prism that I can get out any time I like, and turn everything into rainbows. I forgot, there's also his folding footrule and a spirit level and the spare fretsaw blades, but the fretsaw and hacksaws are too big so they are kept in the Kitchen, which is where we use them, as the kitchen table is best for clamping the wood to.

Keeping on going, you come to the sticking-out end of the sofa that is in the angle of the window wall and the fireplace wall. But tucked in almost behind the end of the sofa is a useful sort of thin upright cabinet. On top of it sits Granpie's old cat's whisker wireless set that he made himself. And inside on the shelves are things like writing and drawing paper, pencils and rubber and crayons and a bottle of fountain pen ink, a toy printing set and a stencil outfit, scissors and a bottle of paste, the chess set because we use it a lot and it's handy there, and my stamp album and packet of stamp hinges. My Auntie Marjorie is a great stamp-collector, but she keeps her albums upstairs in her room.

Right, we've got to the sofa.

It is old, grey, shiny, squashy and comfortable, and it's big enough for two people. It is where Granpie sits to read the morning paper, to have forty winks after lunch, and to smoke his once-a-day-after-tea-time pipe. At those times, unless I am sitting up at the table drawing or crayonning or doing my stamps, I sit on the sofa too, and read quietly.

You have to be good, at Granpie's.

Well, fairly good. Though Acton Grannie does say I'm as stubborn as a mule.

However, that's only to do with vests and things, which I'll explain later.

After the sofa comes Grannie sitting by the Cosy-Stove in her wooden armchair with her feet on the fender to keep warm. On the right of the fireside is a squashy old easy-chair that Grannie doesn't sit in because it's too low. And behind it, on the right of the fireplace, is a black and gold bookcase where a few special things are kept, like the square wood and glass box for looking at Granpie's plate photos of Greece and the Holy Land. And his amazing Stereoscope, with the huge eye-pieces like looking through goggles, and the picture postcards you look at aren't pictures any more, but real places - like our one of Trafalgar Square and the lions - that you could walk into and all around behind things and out again the other side

There are a few more ordinary things kept in the bookcase as well, like the Happy Families that Grannie can play if Granpie helps her, and the Dominoes, Lexicon, Snap, Spillikins and Draughts. Also my bag of glass marbles that go with the big wooden Solitaire board, which is a good brain-teaser and another handy thing for their forty winks time.

So you see, there is always a lot to do here, and a lot to play with.

And that's a thing I like about Granpie's . . . the games and toys and tools stay put. There's a place for them all and you know where to find them.

Not like home, where things keep getting changed and moved around. And there'd be nowhere to put it all . . .

That's strange, when you think about it . . . our house is big, but no room. And here is small, but room for stacks of stuff.

And another thing . . .

At home, I'm just a child, and have to either help or keep out of the way. But here at Granpie's . . .

Well, it's nice, but also makes me feel a bit uncomfortable, as if I'm supposed to be somebody special, when I know I'm not.

For instance, Acton Grannie sometimes asks me if I'll play the piano for her. So we go into the Drawing Room and I play the piece my mother has taught me that week from *Piano Pieces for Beginners*. I play it as well as I can, to please her, but I know it's only baby stuff because I'm just starting. Yet Grannie listens with a far-away look on her face, and then says in a sort of hushed voice, "That was beautiful! You've a lovely touch, child, you must keep up your piano."

Which is kind of her.

But embarrassing.

It's the same with drawings and poems. Granpie thinks they're so marvellous, as if no one had ever done such a thing before. I remember sitting at the table here when I was really little, and writing a truly awful poem about me being small but-if-I-eat-my-porridge-up-I'll-soon-be-big-and-tall, and Granpie sent it to a magazine but they didn't answer.

Why did I write such a thing? I wouldn't have written it at home.

Even now that I'm big, and even though I do a lot of grown-up stuff with Granpie like sawing and gluing and developing photos, I also do a great deal more playing with toys here than I do at home.

Is that just because the toys are here? Or because I'm playing at being little?

164

Even when I'm doing grown-up things, now I come to think of it, while I'm over at Acton I have to be very little-girl-obedient.

Is being-a-little-girl something I put on when I come through the front door, the way I put on my Acton overall? Which is another thing I didn't tell you about . . . something I have to do, that I never do at home except for helping in the Kitchen.

Oh Botheration!

Why is thinking about things so confusing?

It's what my Dad calls an Infernal Nuisance, so I'll stop doing it.

Here we are! We've been all the way round the room and back to the chiffonier. It is elegantly handsome with its carved wood and alcoves and pillars and the mirror along the back.

But when I see it, I just . . think . . . *meals!*

My mum's meals are equal best in all the world, *but* . . . I can't help knowing how hard it has been for her cooking them, *and* . . . the boarders' eyes and the washing-up afterwards . . .

At Granpie's, all we have to do is enjoy it after Mrs Liddington has cooked it. Each day has its own meal, the same every week, because that is how Granpie and Acton Grannie like it. Saturday is always roast and treacle sponge, and Tuesday (the other day I used to come when I was little) is Irish Stew and Great Old. And the moment I open the chiffonier drawers and take out the white cloth with green lines round the edge, and the old cork mats with the border of little square brown and white beads, and the napkins in their bone rings, and set the table, and reach down the cruet from the top chiffonier shelf . . . I start thinking of the deliciousness of the rich peppery gravy and the carrots and peas and potatoes and tender meat . . . and the lovely smell of it coming up the passage from the Kitchen.

Mrs Liddington is tall and thin with dark hair in a bun and wears a green-and-yellow cotton print overall, the sort you put on like a sleeveless coat and wrap all around you and tie at the back with strings. She comes for a few hours every day except Sunday to do a little cleaning and cook the meal and wash up before she goes home. That's nice!

It's really a holiday feeling, not having to wash up, only help clear the table and take out the wooden crumb tray and the little

165

long fluffy brush like a squirrel's tail, brush the crumbs off the table-cloth, open the front of the Cosy-Stove and scoot them into the fire.

Then my tea-time job is to help Granpie set out the cold tea. And . . . the moment I pull Granpie's chair out of the way (from where he sits at the chiffonier end of the table, to carve the roasts and dish out the stews and puddings) and make enough room to open the bottom doors of the chiffonier . . . oh my! . . . it's enough to make anyone greedy, just the sugary-honey-strawberry-jammy scents and the sight of the lovely glass cake-stand that I lift out and put on the table.

Granpie and I butter the bread, dollop out some jam neatly into a pretty china dish, and set out a new jar of potted beef-and-ham or shrimp paste, and maybe in the summer a special treat of strawberries with what he calls a pottle of cream in a little card-board pot. And then we put our heads together, feeling as if it's the fairies all over again, and unpick the knots in the flat paper string round the cake-box, and open it up to see what is in it.

I'm allowed to take the cakes out and arrange them on a paper doily on the cake-stand, one for each of us and one for Auntie Marjorie if she's there, or to keep for her till she gets back, and maybe an extra one for Granpie and me to have half each. Sometimes he has bought meringues and iced fancies from Fuller's and sometimes it's coffee-slices-and-a-cherry and lemon-slices-with-crystallised-lemon from 'The Lantern' tea-shop up by the station.

So you can see that it's very enjoyable in Acton Grannie's Dining Room, like a special once-a-week treat. And cosy, too, especially in winter with the doors of the stove open at Grannie's and my backs, and the lamps beginning to be lit out in the street.

It is very family-feeling, just the three or sometimes four of us, and able to do familyish things like going halves with the fancy cakes if we can't make up our minds which would be nicest, and plenty of time to talk over all we've done during the day.

Sometimes there's an interruption.

Sometimes Carwardine's Grocer's van comes in the middle of tea!

Everything stops, but it's a very happy stop.

Mr Carwardine says, "Whoa there!" and hitches the reins and climbs down from the box. Granpie goes round the back of the van to see what he's got and to give the order. And I fetch sugar lumps and give them to Beauty and Jean, the two horses, the way I do for the big horses in the Council stables. Sometimes Beauty and Jean are busy finishing off their nosebags, and toss their heads up to get the last bits of oats and stuff, and blow down their noses and the chaff comes flying out.

Things like Mr Carwardine coming don't stop the comfy family feeling.

They are part of it.

But there are other things that don't feel so good. Definitely uncomfortable, in fact.

3

SOMETIMES A PLACE SUDDENLY CHANGES

Most times when I go into the Dining Room on a Saturday Grannie is just my usual Grannie with her black eye patch over her missing eye and the other one blind and not looking anywhere, and her bits of straight white hair very thin in places so that you can see her pink head. I go and stand close beside her chair and tell her about school or Guides or home, and that's all right. It's not very lively, but quite comfortable and happy.

But one day when I went in I got such a fright, I nearly ran away. Grannie had thick grey curly hair, and where her black patch ought to have been she had a new eye that was looking straight at me.

It was horrible. Like an ogre.

When I got over the shock I realised it was a wig and a glass eye. But I still don't like them.

On the days when she decides to wear them, Grannie just *isn't* ... she's like someone or something else, and although of course I mustn't mention the fact, and still have to go close, I hate having to, in case that bright blue eye turns and fixes me with an awful ghastly stare.

On those days, the Dining Room isn't cosy and comfortable any more.

Another thing that changes it, is when there's what Miss Fazackerly used to call A Bit Of An Atmosphere. Such as, for instance, over vests and things, that I said I would explain.

"Let's see if you're wearing your Liberty Bodice," Acton Grannie sometimes says in the winter.

But as she can't see, she puts her hand up my skirt to find out. Which I *hate*. And anyway, I'm not wearing one.

A Liberty Bodice, in case you don't know, is shaped like a short vest with a rather high neck. It is made of white cotton with sort of extra seams - flat, longways seams - to make it stronger and thicker. And round the bottom edge are buttons for attaching suspenders to, so as not to have to wear a suspender belt to keep up the black wool stockings that you're supposed to wear at my silly school in winter.

It's a proper babyish thing and I had to wear one when I was little. But not now.

Especially not now that I've decided never, ever, to wear stockings again in my whole life. Who needs stockings? They are such a silly nuisance, always twisting round or wrinkling down or making you feel hot and prickly when you want to run and run, and then cool down afterwards.

So the way it goes is:

"Come on, now, let me feel!"

"Aw . . . Grannie!"

"You naughty girl, you're not wearing it! And those long bare legs in this chilly weather . . . you'll catch your death of cold!"

"I won't! Truly I won't, Grannie!"

"Nonsense! I know you, with your colds and coughs, and your dear Mother always having to rub you with camphorated oil. Now, see that you wear your Liberty Bodice like a good girl, d'you hear?"

"I won't! *Nobody* wears them any more! I *can't!*"

"Hmph! Go your own way then, my lady! You're as stubborn as a mule!"

So then there is an Atmosphere, and the comfortable feeling of

169

h

being at Granpie's has gone. To tell the truth, it's not they who make the Atmosphere, because once it's over they don't mention it again. Everything goes on as happily as ever, on the outside, so it's just *me* . . . I feel *awful*, because Grannie means to be kind, and there is a badness and blackness over everything because I haven't been *good*.

Vests are different. When it's hot weather I often leave them off by-accident-on-purpose, but I always mean to put it on again for coming to Acton so as not to hurt Grannie's feelings. If I've forgotten to, I can say I'm sorry. Because I really am.

However . . .

Vests are still what my Dad calls A Sore Subject.

Did I tell you about Acton Grannie's knitting, with the huge needles? It's my vests she's knitting. With soft white lamb's-wool, in big loopy stitches and odd-shaped gaps where the dropped ones didn't get picked up quite right. I don't like wearing them, but I do, because it's kind of her. Anyway they're the only ones I've got, she makes so many. But it's a dreadful embarrass-ment at school, because of having to wear vests and knickers for gym. Mine are like horrible old lop-sided spiders'-webs full of holes.

If I arrive at Granpie's front door and suddenly remember that I've forgotten, I go hot all over and hope Grannie won't want to have a feel. But she usually does.

"Oh!" she says, sounding surprised and disappointed. "You're not wearing your vest!"

"Oh Grannie, I'm *sorry!* I just forgot."

"You do wear them?"

"Of *course* I do, Grannie . . . they're nice and soft! It was just I was in a hurry and I forgot."

"Ah well then . . . never mind."

All the same, she does mind, and she's sad. And I feel bad, and all mixed up and muddled inside. Because partly I'm ashamed and sorry for hurting her feelings, and partly I'm cross with myself for spoiling *my* nice happy day.

No matter which, Acton Grannie's Dining Room is all Atmosphere instead of comfiness.

Talking of black stockings reminds me of the winter before last, when we were all sliding on the Park Pond and I went through the ice. I was boiling hot from running and sliding and I peeled off my wet stockings and had to squelch all the way home with my legs pink and steaming like kettles, holding these awful, sodden, soggy, dripping black objects. I was sure everyone must be looking.

That's when I decided never to wear stockings again if I could help it. Though I don't think I had any luck that winter, as I was only ten.

It also reminds me of the year we had a Heat Wave in March. I can remember playing in the garden at home and begging to be allowed to take off my jersey and my black stockings. But I wasn't.

"Cast ne'er a Cloot till May be Oot!" said my mother, laughing. "Never mind, my darling, the weather changes so quickly, and Better Safe Than Sorry!"

It was no use looking up at our big may tree and hoping the blossom would have come out early, because my mother said they called it the hawthorn when she was a girl and lived in Scotland, and that May meant the month.

You might think it odd, about Scotland, considering that her mother is my Devonshire Grannie and comes from Dartmouth. So perhaps I should tell you what my Mum says, that my Grandad was Secretary to Admiral Lord Fairfax on his Flagship, which I think sounds very grand and exciting, and soon after my mother was born the Admiral took my Grandad up to the Scottish Borders to go on being Secretary to him on his new estate. So of course all the family went too, and lived within sight of the Eildon Hills until the Admiral died when my mother was twelve.

My Mum teases herself by saying she's a Devon Dumpling, which she isn't, because she's tall and strong. But she feels Scottish and sounds Scottish. And I know she misses the country where she was brought up, by the way she sings her Scottish songs. Especially *My Ain Folk,* which is the one that goes:

'It's, oh, but I'm longing for my ain folk,
Though they be but lowly, poor and plain folk.
I'm far across the sea,
But, oh, I long to be
At home in dear old Scotland wi' my ai - n folk.'

171

*   *   *   *

Anyway, to get back to the subject, it is strange that when I'm at Granpie's the only place anything uncomfortable happens is the Dining Room. Strange that a place can change from good to bad in the twinkling of an eye.

That's what happened today, which is why I've got this subject on the brain. Not that it was anything too terrible, I suppose, but . . .

It so happened that my Auntie Marjorie was here at lunch-time and not up in Piccadilly where she works, even on a Saturday morning usually, but she was home early today. Auntie Marjorie is what I call her, of course, but it looks a bit soppy written down so I'll say 'Aunt M' from now on. She is fat and jolly and kind and has brown fingers from smoking like a chimney, and wears things like brown cardigan suits with a peachy silk tie-bow blouse and a long loop of amber beads hanging down over her comfy-cushiony front.

Anyway, we'd only that minute finished a second helping of potatoes and gravy. Aunt M sat back, wiped her mouth with her napkin, and said in her cheery, chuckly voice, "Well lass, how d'you feel about a swim next Saturday?"

My insides stopped being happy, and dropped into a big black hole.

I said, "Oh, *no*, Aunt M!"

"But, oh *yes!*" she said, still smiling her jolly smile. "Never mind, it's one of those things up-with-which-you-have-to-put! And we'll enjoy ourselves at the Pool afterwards, won't we, and maybe have an ice-cream if Mr Dixon will let you! Have you been brushing your teeth properly?"

Aunt M likes Mr Dixon and they have fierce political arguments over the top of my head, merrily shouting to each other about Chamberlain and that-so-and-so-Hitler and things I don't understand, while Mr Dixon's holding me down with one hand and drilling away with the other, the noise enough to bust your head, and the guggle-tube guggling away and me going "Er-r-r-gh! Er-r-r-gh!" because he's hurting me, but he can't hear for the racket and doesn't take any notice anyway. It's like a nightmare.

I know I have soft teeth, which my mother says is because

172

when she was having me nobody knew about orange-juice, so they're always needing fillings. Also, it's true that because Mr Dixon's Dreaded Dental Surgery is in Chiswick we go to Chiswick Baths afterwards and have a very good time, because Aunt M is a wonderful swimmer and she had me taught to swim there years ago, with the Baths Attendant holding me in a big leather loop on the end of a line.

But . . . why do I have to go to her dentist, anyway? He is *horrible!* I admit he did once give me a board-game afterwards, about things like Gibbs' Fairy castle and Giant Decay, but that doesn't make up for him hurting me so much and paying no attention.

I totally, utterly *dread* going.

Fancy telling me just when I was looking forward to the treacle pudding!

I wonder why Aunt M enjoys shouting politics so much? Perhaps she finds it boring going to work every day, and Mr Dixon makes a change?

That reminds me about something I find puzzling.

My Auntie Marjorie and my father Frank are sister and brother, as I may have mentioned. Now, Aunt M does not look at all like my idea of someone who went to college, yet she did, and is a BSc Chem. And my father looks exactly right for a college sort of person, being tall and thin and bony and thoughtful, but he didn't.

Ah well, you might say, you have to be clever to go to college, don't you? So perhaps he wasn't clever enough? Or not as clever as his sister?

That, however, is where you'd be wrong. I've never seen a book of Aunt M's with a prize sticker inside the front cover, in fact I'm not sure that she is much interested in books at all. Whereas my Dad had *five* prize books from his school in Hampstead, including a Cherry Kearton one on Bird Photography, and a lovely Wild Flower one, and British Birds by W.H. Hudson. And I'm sure he knows a lot, and thinks a great deal, even though he keeps it to himself.

Well then, you might think, perhaps he didn't *want* to go to college. Maybe he had a very interesting job that he liked better?

But that isn't true, either, because I asked my Mum what he did

173

before the Great War, after he left school, and she told me he had tried being a journalist, but that he is gentle and sensitive and hated trying to ferret out people's secrets and make them unhappy. And then, because he is good at drawing as well as writing, he went into a draughtsman's office which, she said, meant sitting at a desk in a room with lots of other people, drawing machines and things.

"I'm not sure what went wrong with that," she said. "Maybe it was rush, rush, rush from morning to night and being told to hurry up and get your drawing finished, or . . . " my Mum laughed, and the dimples came in her cheeks, " . . . maybe he just doesn't like machines! We'd rather he was singing, and happy, wouldn't we?"

You bet we would!

I bet it's more fun . . . no, more - more absolutely magically fantastically wonderful . . . being a Covent garden opera singer who *hasn't* been to college, than being a BSc who *has* . . . and does what Aunt M does.

Because she's a Chemical Indexer, and I haven't the foggiest what that means, but she took me up to Piccadilly once and showed me what she does, which is to sit in a small stuffy room all by herself and cut out chemical names and facts from journals and stick them on cards and file them in sort of shoe-box files with a metal rod running through them.

It must be very boring.

But I still didn't understand why she went to college and my Dad didn't. So I asked Granpie.

He sounded pleased to be asked. He likes giving me plenty of information.

"Ah! Now then!" he said, and did a little hrmphing cough into his pointy beard. "We're a Huguenot family, as you know . . ." (which I did) " . . . and it's a Huguenot custom that if there's only enough money to send one child to University, it is always the eldest who goes."

Hmm. And ho hum!

It's not what I'd call a reasonable explanation.

Everything to do with grown-ups is puzzling.

The last thing about the Dining Room suddenly getting uncomfortable is to do with dying.

You might think I'm making it up, that it's only in this room the subject crops up, but it's true.

For instance, the time Granpie gave me the Girls' Annual and I found he had cut 'Best Blacks' out of it, so that I wouldn't read about funerals, and I had to pretend and kid him on that I hadn't noticed . . . that was when I was sitting on the sofa with him before his forty winks.

That was a very bothersome feeling. I don't know how to explain it except the way I did before, almost as if I were the grown-up and he was the child. Like when you turn a snow-scene upside down and the snow falls the wrong way.

Another time was two or three years ago when we were sitting up at the table enjoying Saturday tea, and Granpie had his wireless on. Not his cat's-whisker set with the head-phones, but his ordinary one that we can all listen to, that lives on the little shelves above the sofa with his baccy tin and pipes. They wanted to hear the News and I wasn't paying much attention.

Suddenly there was a dreadful empty silence. Granpie switched off the set and he and Grannie clattered their cups down, and sat staring at nothing, as if turned to stone.

Then Granpie said in a strange unbelieving voice, "The *King* is *dead!*"

It sounded like the finish of everything.

I know that Granpie thought a great deal of King George V, and in fact looks quite like him.

But . . . he looked *frightened* . . . as if it were The End Of The World.

"Poor Queen Mary," said Grannie in a flat voice, and that was the end of that.

I still don't really understand. I mean, why one King is different from another King. But it certainly wasn't a nice family-feeling interruption like Mr Carwardine.

I'll hurry up and tell you the worst one, that only happened the Saturday before last, and then I can stop going on about horrible things and bung them all in a black hole and forget about them.

Oh help . . . ! No, I can't . . . it's the Dreaded Mr Dixon next week!

Never mind, There-Are-Worse-Troubles-At-Sea, as Granpie

always says.

Anyway, the reason this is worst is:

1. I can't tell anyone.
2. I don't know what to make of it.
3. It scares me, which I expect it shouldn't do when I'm
   going to be twelve in twenty-seven days time, but . . .

It was raining cats-and-dogs and I had a cold and Granpie said I
was to stay with Grannie while he went round the corner to the
baker's.

The minute he went out, Acton Grannie said, "Get out the little
green book with gold lettering on the back from the top shelf of
the bookcase and read me something, like a good girl. Be quick,
now! That's right . . . read me where it's marked on the page that
the ribbon's in."

I did, and it was something about Heaven, and God, but . . . it
is so strange, I don't know what I read or the name of the book or
anything . . . I was sort of shivering all over because Grannie
sounded peculiar, and was wearing her wig and ogre eye which
made it worse, and anyway nothing like that had ever happened
before. I didn't even know that she knew what books were in the
black bookcase, or what was in them.

Then she said, "Thank you. Put it back now in the same
place . . . that's right, good girl. Now come close and listen to
what I say. Will you promise me something?"

I said, "Yes, Grannie!" in a tiny little voice, because I didn't
know what it was going to be . . . but what else can you say?

"Promise me," she said, "that when I'm gone you'll look after
Granpie. You *will* look after him, won't you?"

And I said, "Yes Grannie, of course I will. I promise!"

And that was that, and Granpie was coming in the front door,
all wet and happy with a brown loaf and a bag of sugar buns and
his big black brolly.

But . . .

What does it mean, to look after Granpie?

It's *Granpie* who looks after *me* . . . isn't it?

176

4

GRANPIE AND ME

Granpie takes me everywhere.

You know the way you see other children out with their
parents? Well, that's only a once-in-a-blue-moon thing, for us.
Like when we go on the top of the 65 bus to Kew Gardens about
once a year, if my Mum can get away, and do all her favourite
things . . . walking under the bending low branches of the cherry-
blossom trees, and having a picnic by the lake with the Muscovy
ducks . . . and buying Maids-of-Honour tarts to take home, from
the little shop opposite the bus stop.

But that, and the towing path to Richmond just sometimes, and
rowing in a skiff with my Dad up to Twickenham Lock, just
once . . . that's about all.

Because my Mum is so busy.

Anywhere you can possibly imagine that it's fun to go, it's
always Granpie and me. He loves it. And it's always his idea.

I wouldn't know where to go, anyway. So it's not *me* saying,
"Please can we . . . ?" It's always *him* saying, "Let's go to . . . "
wherever it is, and me saying, "Yes, let's!" And we have a

177

wonderful time.

He takes me just everywhere . . . the Zoo, and fairs on the Common, and the Whit Monday Horse Parade with the costers' carts piled high with fruit, and the Pearly King and Queen, ponies and traps, soldiers with horses pulling gun-carriages, Lamertons' Removals with six dapple-grey ponies pulling the huge van and tossing red plumes on their heads, the Council carts with the shire horses, and all the coal merchants with their wagons painted up like new and the horses spanking smart with braided tails and manes, and their heads proud and tossing high with jingling brasses, and bells on the points of the great shining black collars . . . and up to London to feed the ducks on the Serpentine, and to Trafalgar Square and Madame Tussaud's and the Tower and the Changing of the Guard, and lots of times to the Natural History Museum and the Science Museum in South Kensington.

It isn't only the famous places . . . Granpie turns every walk into an adventure and finds something interesting to do, wherever we go.

He doesn't hurry past the place where the trains disappear under the bridge in a great billowing-out of smoke and smuts. No fear! Instead, he buys a train-spotter's notebook and we stand at the railings to wait for them coming and spot the numbers of the tank-engines and the names of the expresses.

When it's the conker season he collects them with me, and gets quite excited, saying, "What a beauty!" and "Bless my soul! I never saw so many in all my born days!" We love the hard prickly green outsides, and the fascinating feeling of opening up the soft inside, like white calf-skin, to find the glossy brown gorgeous chestnut that no one has ever seen before, and is so beautiful that it hurts in your heart, you can scarcely bear it. And when they get old and dull he holds them steady for me to make holes through with his gimlet, and thread them on string to take to school.

As for the Council Stables, most people just walk past the cobbled entrance and keep on down the road, minding their own business. But not Granpie! He walks boldly but politely, down past the steaming manure heap, holding me by the hand . . . or he did when I was small . . . and on down the slope to the open stalls and the ring of the blacksmith's hammer and the stamping of hoofs. We stand to one side, keeping out of the way, and watch them grooming, and polishing, and the pulling out of the shoe-nails with huge pincers, and the puffing of the bellows, and the shaping of the red-hot shoes . . . the hissing and clanging, and "Whoa!" and "There, boy!" and the smell of the singeing horn as the hot shoe goes on, and the blacksmith looking like Wayland-Smith in *Puck of Pook's Hill* in his leather apron. If anyone looks our way, Granpie - with his hat in his hand down at his side - says, "Is this all right? We won't get in the way." And the man gives a happy laugh and a nod, or says, "That's all right, guv'nor . . . you stay put!"

Once we saw them washing one of the shire horse's beautiful feathery feet in a big galvanised bath, till he gave a tremendous kick with his hind hoof and the water sloshed out like a flood all over lots of things including my white socks and button shoes. Who cares! Though, of course, Granpie did, and got busy drying me off with his pocket-handkerchief. Another time, when I was so little I hadn't even started school . . . I know that, because I was still wearing sun-bonnets . . . one of the men lifted me up onto a horse's back and tried to give me a ride along the yard with Granpie walking along on the other side, and the horse's back was so wide it was like sitting on the floor, only very wobbly, and I bounced a few times and slid off into the man's arms.

Talking about sun-bonnets reminds me of going to the park.

I'll tell you why in a minute.

Because I just had a strange thought.

Why is it always Granpie and me?

Why not my brother?

Or does he go to places with Granpie on different days? I don't think so, though I can't be sure.

But if not, *why* not?

An even stranger thought is . . . why haven't I thought about it before? Things happen the way they happen . . . and I never think about why. Do grown-ups understand the reasons for things? I know that I don't. I can't even begin to imagine it. Things are the way they are, because they *are*.

The only bit I know the answer to, now I come to think about it, is why my brother doesn't come to Acton on Saturdays. That's easy. He is seven now and goes to a school called a Prep School. They have Wednesday afternoons off, but have lessons on

Saturday mornings and cricket and football and things on Saturday afternoons.

So that's that.

But I can't work out about the rest of the outings. We do just sometimes go all three of us, but hardly ever. Perhaps Granpie can't manage with more than one of us at a time. Or perhaps it would bother him, having three people talking to each other instead of two.

Come to think of it, that would be true for Acton as well. And there are other reasons why my brother might not enjoy going over to Granpie's every week. One could be . . . well, Grannie's ogre eye and things like that. Then again, he's very clever. Although he's only seven - nearly eight, actually - he doesn't just *play* chess, he *studies* it. He works out moves from a little book and plays against himself. So Granpie's and my sort of chess might be too easy, even though *we* think it's good and tough, and have great battles.

Another thing he mightn't enjoy is this business of being little-girl-or-boy-obedient. Not that anyone *says* you've got to be. Only it just wouldn't work if everyone wanted to do different things. But if you go along with what Granpie suggests, it works out beautifully.

But I still don't really understand. It's another of these mysterious puzzles that I'd never thought of before.

And when I start, I wish I hadn't.

I just had an *awful* thought.

Does me getting all these questions, and having all these puzzle-thinks, mean I'm getting to be grown-up?

I hope not!

I'd hate to be grown-up . . . doing accounts and paying bills.

What I was going to tell you about was parks, and going to them with Granpie, which is something we both enjoy very much.

"Let's go to Gunnersbury today, shall we?" he'll say. "It's a good long walk, so we'll have to stir our stumps!" And we step it out so as to have plenty of time to explore, and look round Gunnersbury Park Museum, and see the ducks quacking and chasing, and the moorhens stepping all cautious and pointy-toed across the big lilypads.

"How about going to Walpole Park to feed the pigeons?" he'll say another day. And first of all we go to the Corn Chandler's in the Broadway. In front of the counter there's a line of square tins with a different kind of corn or seed in each, and a little metal scoop to shovel out what you want into a paper bag. We know the pigeons' favourite things that'll make them come and roost on our heads and arms, so as well as wheat and stuff we choose Indian corn and hard round black peas.

However, what reminded me of parks, was talking about sun-bonnets. They're babyish things, and old-fashioned, made of flower-print cotton with a frilly brim all round. When I was very little I was made to wear one any time the sun was hot. Granpie would plonk it on my head, before he took me out, and tie it firmly under my chin with its own flower-print cotton strings.

One day when I was little, but big enough to walk everywhere, he and I had been to the park to have a go on the swings and we were on our way home. Although it was getting on for winter I was wearing a sun-bonnet, which is very odd and you might think I'm making it up, but I'm not. All I can think is that Granpie must have decided - the way he decides everything - that the sun was too hot to risk it. Anyway, we were standing side by side at the edge of the main road, waiting till it was safe to cross, when something very strange happened.

All the traffic stopped!

And everyone stood stock still as if someone had cast a spell like in Sleeping Beauty!

I suppose there was a boom from a gun, but all I remember is that Granpie stood to attention and took off his old grey Homburg hat. And because I was little I copied everything he did, and tried to pull my sun-bonnet off and nearly choked on the strings. He straightened it up and shushed me and nothing moved or made a sound for ages.

Because, of course, it was 11 o'clock on November 11th, Armistice Day.

When everything started moving again, Granpie said, "Gentlemen take their hats off but ladies don't."

Which was the first I'd heard about that. I'd seen it in church but without really noticing, except that it was interesting being up in the gallery and counting how many bald heads and how many hats.

I still can't understand why there's a rule like that. I mean, taking hats *off* I can see the reason for, in a way. But if it's right for men, why not for us? What's the difference? After all, women usually have more hair to cover their heads with, so why hats as well?

What I think is, it's what my Dad would call Infernally Stupid.

One of these grown-up things up-with-which-you-have-to-put and not ask why.

I have a best Sunday-go-to-meeting hat of pale green straw with pretend daisies round the brim. The sun comes through in little flecks like light on water.

But it's horribly scratchy to wear.

I *don't like* hats!

When I grow up I am not going to wear hats *ever*.

Granpie does his best to bring me up properly and teach me what is right. Even though he is so interesting to be with, and knows how to have fun, he can be very stern.

I can't ever remember him smacking me. He doesn't have to. Last winter when he'd brought me back home after church and I was feeling in a bad mood, I threw my coat down all anyhow and didn't pick it up when he asked me nicely.

He went very still and straight and said in a cold voice, "Pick your coat up and hang it up properly this instant, or I shall have to be *very angry!*"

I just about went to jelly all over and hurried to do-as-I-was-told.

Granpie is also extremely strict about the Truth.

I tell him riddles and 'Knock-knock' jokes from school, but I'm hopeless at doing April Fools. However, I tried a feeble one on him as we were walking down the road one year, calling out, "Oh, Granpie, you've dropped your hankie!" He turned round to see and I yelled "April Fool!" but his face went grave and he stood there on the pavement and gave me a lecture.

"You are wrong," he said, "and you have misunderstood the

182

situation. If you say that a thing is so, or is not so, then I am entitled to rely on your statement. And if you have told me an Untruth, then it is *you* who are the April Fool . . . not me!"

And we went on walking, while he explained to me in a kindly way the sort of April Fool tricks that were allowable, because they did not offend against the Truth, even though they could still fool you . . . like the usual ones of saying there's a hole in your sock, which of course there is, otherwise you wouldn't be able to get your foot in.

Actually, I find that kind of discussion quite interesting. It's not just that it fits in with Laws, like 'A Guide's Honour is to be Trusted', but it is reasonable, and gives your brain something to think hard about, like doing what Granpie calls Philosophy.

You know when you balance things on weighing scales, it's a bit like that . . . Philosophy Thoughts on one side and all the other things he teaches me on the other, like changing fuses and how to cut wire with the side of the pincers, and how to change a fretsaw blade when you've been stupid enough to break it in the first place because of not holding the fretsaw straight.

When it comes to tools, Granpie is the best ever teacher. No matter what we are doing, he shows me how and then gets me to do it myself. Unless it's something terribly dangerous.

That's funny.

He lets me melt lead and saw wood and even use his treadle lathe and put tools in the chuck.

Yet if I hurt myself, you can tell that he goes all panicked inside, as if I'm a china doll and might fall to pieces. He's always trying to protect me and it's a bit embarrassing sometimes, like when I got a bad cut on the knee at school and I could see him through the window walking as fast as he could, with his head poking forward from his shoulders and looking neither to right nor left but only looking dreadfully anxious . . . until he saw me and found out I was all right.

Of course, I'm not talking about little scrapes and scratches. He never fusses over those. And when I was little, if I fell down and bumped myself he'd pick me up and say, "There, there . . . it's nothing! It'll be well before you're twice married!"

However, there was a bad time when I got walloped in the eye

183

by a hockey stick in the playground when I was six, and was still at my little school, called Miss Burrow's, that I went to before this one. One of the bigger girls was fooling around with a hockey stick and I was behind her as she swung back. All round my left eye came up huge and black and yellow and I had to wear a bandage for weeks. I'm not sure why. It was supposed to be to rest my eye and Take Precautions, though it was probably only Granpie being anxious. It was his idea that I should go to Miss Burrow's school, so I dare say he felt responsible.

Anyway, when I'd had this bandage on for about a fortnight, he went very silent one day as we were coming back from a walk, and suddenly stopped still. He stood behind me, took hold of my shoulders and faced me down the street, and gently slid the bandage up from my eye.

He took a sort of sighing breath and asked in a tight little voice, "What can you see?"

I hate to admit it, but I just said cheerfully, "Oh, nothing much!" meaning that there was nothing special, just houses and trees and things. And then I was sorry I'd been so unkind, and rattled off a list of all the things I could see, so that he'd know I wasn't going blind like Grannie.

Because I knew all along what this was about, even before I came out with what I said, and felt his fear. Not that I meant to hurt him. Not exactly, it just slipped out.

I wonder why? Is it because of him being so serious about something that's really nothing at all? Protecting me as if I'm special, when I'm not?"

I don't know.

Yes, I do! I've got it . . . it just came to me!

It - is - such - a *temptation* . . . to tease grown-ups when they think you are so little that you don't understand anything! They don't realise that, in a flash, you know what they are thinking but not saying, you know what they are afraid of, and what they're hoping. They pretend, and kid you on, and they think you don't know that they're kidding. But you do! And although it's unkind, sometimes you can't stop yourself, and you kid them back.

I keep saying 'grown-ups' and 'them', but really it's only Granpie this happens with, because of him trying to protect me, and hiding what he's thinking.

Never mind . . . he means it for the best.

However, it is an interesting fact that even when you are six, or even five, although you look little, and act little . . . you do not *feel* little.

Now that I'm nearly twelve, I don't feel any older inside than I did when I was five. And when I was five I felt very old indeed.

When I started at Miss Burrow's there were four of us in the first class. The other three had been there for a term before me, and in the cloakroom they showed me the beautiful tin daggers that they had, and I understood that it was babyish of me not to have one, so I made one that evening out of cardboard and painted it in gold and black. It looked real, and was magnificent, but the others laughed at it in a scathing way, although afterwards they agreed to accept me, when they realised I wouldn't be allowed anything better.

It was a grave and serious business we were discussing. We did not feel like little children.

I just thought of something very odd. And how funny life is!

Funny peculiar, that is.

Because all the people in Parliament making laws and discussing terribly serious affairs, could not possibly in a million years feel any older inside themselves than we felt then, talking in the cloakroom at Miss Burrow's.

Yet only a few weeks before, when Granpie had been taking me round to two or three other little schools to see which one was best, a lady had been showing me coloured picture cards of 'S for Sun' and 'U for Umbrella', to see if I knew my letters!

Which I did, because even when he was still pushing me around in the push-chair, Granpie had taught me letters and word-sounding from the street names, and how to count railings and things like that.

Miss Burrow's school had just two teachers and two classrooms and was in an ordinary house, with a playground out the back where the garden would be. But although it was small, it was not in the least silly. As well as the usual lessons we did sensible things like Nature Study, growing beans on blotting-paper and copying drawings from the blackboard of the parts of a flower, or a crab with all its jointed arms and claws. And at Christmas I made a needle-book for my mother, and Granpie's baccy tin, and our teacher gave us each a plain wooden pencil and swirled oil-paints on a bucket of water and let us dip our pencils in so that they came out all marbled in beautiful colours.

By the time I'd been there two years I could read almost anything, and write and spell, and we'd got as far as my favourite long-division, so I was looking forward to going up to the big classroom and learning grown-up stuff.

Yet when Miss Burrow's closed, and Granpie chose this school I'm at now . . . and I don't know why he did, unless it was because of them walking neatly in crocodile, wearing horrible white gloves . . . you'll hardly believe what I was given to do on my first day, when I was seven. Because I could read, I was put to sit up on the high stool at the teacher's desk on the dais, and given a nice big copy of *The Water Babies* to read to the class while the teacher did something else. Then I was asked to help one of the older girls to read. And on some afternoons we made truly awful pretty-pretty jewellery by poking imitation buds and bobbles into a sort of paste stuck onto metal shapes with pins attached.

It's true that I was moved to another class quite soon, and had proper lessons. But I don't actually remember really *learning* anything for the next two years in that room, till I moved up to Miss Jaeger's when I was nine and started parsing sentences and copying maps and reading *Captain's Courageous* and doing 'amo, amas, amat' and all the rest of it. However, since I moved up again last September, it's all gone silly again.

School is a very boring subject.

Also, a pretty scarey fact occurred to me the other day. Since I've been in this classroom, which I'll be in till I'm thirteen, I've realised that . . . because there's only one more class to go . . . the big girls in that class, who seem so dreadfully grown-up, are only fifteen when they leave! So if I don't hurry up and *learn* something, I don't know what it's all been *for!*

Ah me!

There must be some reason why I'm here . . . and surely Granpie knows why?

Because the other things he decides, and the places we go, just couldn't be better.

*   *   *   *

That reminds me.

It's getting to be summery enough to go to Top Locks, which is one of Granpie's and my favourite places, so I hope we go soon.

We go on the top of the bus to Hanwell, and get off and walk up a little road to the left till we get to the canal, and watch the canal boats and the horses pulling them. We help the lock-keeper open the lock-gates by Granpie and me shoving on one of the big black timbers with the white-painted ends, and the lock-keeper shoving on the other one across the canal. Or we go up on the little grey stone arched bridge and look down into a boat sliding underneath, and get a cheery wave.

It's nice thinking about these things, a lot nicer than confusing puzzle thinks, and a million times better than remembering that it's school again on Monday.

However, it's time I told you about the rest of the house.

5

GRANPIE'S STUDY

Turn left out of the Dining Room and straight away turn left again out of the dark passage, and up three triangle-shaped steps that swizzle round to the right again, and you're on the steep straight stairs going up to Granpie's Study.

However, I'll tell you the rest of the upstairs first.

On the left at the top of the stairs is the lavatory and then the bathroom, which Granpie sometimes turns into a dark-room with a red bulb and a blacked-out window and we develop negatives and print them in frames. The bath is really ancient, even a little rusty in places. But it's long and deep and narrow, just right for testing out his boats, the *Exmouth Belle* and the *Starcross*.

Aunt M's room is down the far end of the long passageway and looks out over the garden. I don't go in it much, and anyway it's chock-full of clothes, and stacks of journals and papers, and smells of smoke and moth-balls. However, Aunt M has a wonderful and powerful microscope which she brings downstairs sometimes and shows me her slides of flies' wings and cross-sections of plant stems.

Granpie and Grannie's room is at the front end of the passage. It looks out over the street and has a door out to a tiny balcony, where we hung a flag at the Coronation. As well as the usual things like a marble washstand and a gigantic wardrobe, it has:

1. An uncomfortable sort of black-and-white picture of a blindfold lady sitting on a globe, playing a harp and looking miserable.
2. The round box where Granpie keeps his shiny stiff collars, because they can't lie flat, but have to stay neck-shaped.
3. A beautiful flat box of polished wood with a little catch on the front, and when you lift the lid there are all these specially shaped compartments with labelled rocks and fossils in them. My favourites are the fossil sea-horse, the granite with little mirrors of mica, and best of all the piece of pure white quartz with just one polished patch, like water, where you can look right down into the heart of the rock.

Next door to their bedroom is a very uninteresting but useful Spare Room where I sleep if I stay the night in the holidays.

Ignore that and keep straight on down the passage as if you're going back to Aunt M's room. Just before you get to it there's a door on your left. Open the door, and you're in Granpie's Study.

It's a little room. The left-hand wall has some watercolour pictures of sea and sky and sand in Guernsey that Granpie painted a long time ago, and a framed certificate, and photographs. There isn't room for furniture on that wall.

Straight ahead is the window looking out across the yard to the next-door house. In front of the window is Granpie's desk with papers and box-files and a spike with bills on, and his huge old Olivetti typewriter that weighs a ton and can't be shifted, so I sit in his swivel chair if I want to type something.

The other two walls are all bookcases from floor to ceiling. Two of the shelves are for special things that I'll tell you about later, but the rest is books, and books, and books and more books, like a library.

Now, here is a strange thing.

At home, I don't think there's a single book in the house that I haven't read. Well, not the guests' private books in their own rooms, of course, except Mr Grüning's Kiplings that I'm about half-way through. But all my Dad's prize books and his *Robinson Crusoe* and *Call of the Wild* and things. Even the old Devon Gazettes I've read from cover to cover. There's nothing I like better, if I get the chance, than to curl up in the low armchair in our Dining Room, and read on and on till someone stops me to go and fetch something, or to help with the beds or in the Kitchen.

But here, at Acton? No! Never!

There is just - so - *much* to do . . . it sounds silly, but I never even *think* about books here, except for Aunt M's *Yellow Fairy Book* that I sometimes read when I'm here on holiday. And Granpie's books are dull-and-dusty-looking, and old, from his college days, and for studying and writing sermons.

Because Granpie was a minister.

He didn't want to be a minister, and only became one to please his mother! That's what he says!

Just recently, though, he explained to me that it is another of these Huguenot tradition things, that all the sons in their family have always been Congregational ministers back to the year dot. Except, of course, my father isn't.

I just thought . . .

Could that be why he wasn't sent to college? Because he wouldn't be a minister?

Surely not?

It certainly isn't a thing I could ever ask him, because I wouldn't dare. Even if I did, he'd tell me I was too inquisitive for my own good, and to get to pot out of it.

* * * * ! ! !

Sorry . . . that wasn't even the beginnings of a poetry-think, just me having a laugh at the very idea of my Dad being a minister!

He has some wicked thoughts, though in a nice sort of way.

For instance, on Sundays, hundreds of people walk *up* our road to the Roman Catholic Church, and a very few walk *down* our road to the Baptist Church, and my Dad is very naughty about

190

both of them. The streaming multitudes going *up*, he calls the Roaming Calf-licks. And the faithful few going the other way, just one family actually, he calls the Prophets of the Groves and has quiet laughs inside himself because of the fact that they always carry umbrellas no matter what the weather, which he thinks highly appropriate to Baptists and total immersion.

I didn't get that bit, and had to ask him.

The reason he knows about the Prophets of the Groves is because of singing in Mendelssohn's *Elijah*. If you heard him singing those Recitatives, and the wonderful deep Aria where Elijah prays:

> 'Lord God of A - braham,
> I - saac and I - srael,
> This day . . . let it be known that
> Thou - art - God
> And that I - am thy - servant!'

you'd know that my Dad is quite the opposite of wicked, about anything that matters. His making fun is just jokes with words, like the 'Prophets' thing being because their surname happens to be Groves, not because he really thinks they feast at Jezebel's table the way it says in the music.

At least all the hordes going up and down the road set us a good example. I mean, they go to church, and my mother and father don't, but I don't know why.

I know they used to go, once upon a time. Grown-ups are very confusing and life is full of *ifs*. Because *if* they hadn't once upon a time gone to church, I wouldn't have been born . . . or would I? . . . anyway, I wouldn't be *me*.

The reason I know this is because although they were in the same opera chorus, and liked the look of each other, and got talking to each other at rehearsals because they had the same sort of bunny-rabbit tea-mug, it was only when they discovered that they both went to the same Congregational church that they got round to thinking they might get married.

Oh, help! I'm getting too many thoughts all at once!

Because here's an even bigger *if*, that my Mum told me about, the same as she told me the one I just said.

This is such a weird *if*, I don't like to think about it, and don't

191

really want to say it but . . .

If a certain minister hadn't got . . . *drunk!* . . . I wouldn't have
been born! That is potty, but it's the truth. I won't say where it
happened, or when, but my mother's family long, long ago used
to be C of E, until one day the vicar or whatever got up into the
pulpit and was . . . what I said . . . and Devonshire Grannie walked
out with all her family and never went back, but became a
Congregationalist instead. So if that hadn't happened, my Mum
and Dad wouldn't have met in the same church and got round to
thinking about getting married.

Here is an even worse *if*.

It makes me go all strange inside, like falling through Space,
whirling away into the stars and dissolving into nothing . . .

If my mother's fiancé had not been killed in the Great War, I
wouldn't have been born. She still has his photo and his engage-
ment ring. If there had been no War, if he hadn't been in the
Army, and killed in action, they'd have been married, and . . .

Where would I be, if I wasn't born?

Would I know where I was?

Would *God* know where I was? Or wouldn't I *be*, at all?

What does it mean, not to be?

It's like Eternity . . . there is no picture in my mind to tell me
what it means.

It is all very strange.

And if you think about it, *everything* seems to be *ifs*. Yet it fits
together.

My mother sang to my father before she knew who he was.

The way it happened was this.

Some time after the Admiral died there was no work for
Devonshire Grandad in Scotland, so the family had to come to
London, and my mother studied singing there with Madame
Marchesi, and sang as a soloist in concerts and oratorios. During
the War she went with a group to sing to the troops in France and
to the wounded soldiers back home in hospital, and on the day she
went to a hospital in Oxford, my father was there being taught to
walk again after being shell-shocked at the Battle of the Somme.
But they didn't meet till years later.

And that, come to think of it, is another *if*, because *if* my mother hadn't been brought up to think it was wrong to work on Sundays, she wouldn't have done what she did do . . . turned down some important engagements that would have Led-To-Other-Things . . . and she would have gone on being a soloist, and maybe even famous, and not joined the opera chorus, and not met my father. And the only reason *he* was in opera was because of having decided, after the War, that singing was the only thing he was good at.

So it's amazing, how things fit together.

Does it just happen? Or does God have a plan?

It's like my Mum said, the day she was telling me all this while we were washing up together on a Sunday . . . I suppose it was because of it being a Sunday, and yet having to work so hard, that brought it into her mind . . . and she said, "So you see, my darling, you never know what life has in store for you!"

Then she stopped dish-mopping the plates, and her voice went all far-away, and wondering, and she said, "I prayed for him, too . . . long before I met him."

I said, "What do you mean?"

Her hands started moving again, and she smiled, and gave a little laugh, and said, "When I was not all that much older than you, I used to pray for the man I would one day marry . . . it was such a strange thought, to know that he was in the world some-where, living his own life, all unknown to me."

My Mum hardly ever says things like that.

Granpie *never* does . . . not ever.

It gives me a shock, coming into Granpie's Study and being reminded that he was a minister.

Perhaps I shouldn't say *was*. He is retired, and he doesn't wear a clergyman's collar. But I suppose he still *is*. He does locum preaching sometimes, and is Father Christmas for them at Bethnal Green and things like that.

But most of the time I forget, until I come up here and see all these Commentaries and boxes of sermon notes and books on the Old Testament and the New Testament and the Life of Jesus. Unless he has to, like when Devonshire Grannie died, he never mentions God, or Jesus, or praying, or anything of the sort. And whereas my Mum would say, "If a thing is worth doing it's worth

j

doing well," Granpie says his usual, "Don't spoil the ship for a ha'porth of tar!"

What Granpie is interested in is *things* . . . what makes them go, and how they work.

And here is the secret . . . what he wanted to be was, not a minister, but an *engineer!*

He was a good minister, I expect, but in his spare time he'd do as many engineering sort of things as he could.

On the special shelves in his Study are working models that he has made. As well as the boats, that need an expedition up to the Round Pond in Kensington Gardens to give them a good run, there is also a beam-engine like the ones used for pumping water from mines, and a trip-hammer, and a stationary engine with a fly-wheel and a tall smoke-stack like Stephenson's 'Rocket'. They are just like the full-size ones in the Science Museum, where he loves to go so that we can push the buttons and watch the pistons and all the parts working smoothly and strongly together.

When we go on holiday it's nearly always to Exmouth, because he used to live there and loves going on the Great Western Railway, that he calls 'the good old G.W.R.'. The first thing he does when we've found our seats is leave Auntie Marjorie to keep an eye on the cases, and hurry along with me to see the engine. He has a word with the railwayman oiling the wheels and connecting up the couplings, and points out things to me in the cab high above us, where the engine-driver and the fireman are getting steam up.

I think it's pretty exciting myself, with the hissing and the steam, and everyone enjoying every minute of it, and the shouts of porters, and pigeons flying up through the sunlight and smoke, and Granpie and me hurrying back in case they go without us.

Soon after we get to Exmouth we go for a cruise over to a place called The Warren on the *Starcross*, which is the boat that Granpie's model is an exact copy of. Once she is under way, Granpie takes me up to the bridge, waits politely, and then asks, "I wonder whether I might take my young granddaughter to see the engine-room?"

So off we go. No one ever seems to say 'No' to Granpie. And it is pretty fascinating, standing at the open doorway and staring down into the depths, with the darkness and the hot oily smell, and the throb and thump of the engines, and the huge pistons bending and stretching like big dinosaur legs, relentlessly unhurrying.

Granpie would like to stop there for ages. You can tell.

So you can understand him making his own *Starcross*. You should just see her go, steaming across the Pond all smart in her black and red and white paint, with smoke coming out of her funnel and the wake churning out behind, while I run fast to the other side to turn her and send her back to Granpie. And then Granpie feels too stiff to go on bending over the water and fiddling with the boilers, and takes off his summer panama hat and mops the bald top of his head with his pocket-handkerchief.

"Ah, well!" he says, "Anno Domini!" . . . which means he's not feeling as young as he used to . . . and he takes his gold watch from his waistcoat pocket, slips off its little shammy-leather cover, pops the gold lid open, snaps it shut again and says, "Time to be off!" He wipes *Starcross* dry and sits her carefully back in the carrier bag with the cloth and the meths bottle, and we go and get an ice-cream from the Stop-Me-And-Buy-One.

It's strange, standing here in Granpie's Study and thinking about holidays. Other thoughts come into my head at the same time. For instance, if they manage to arrange for some kind person to look after Grannie while we're away, why can't they find somebody to look after the boarders, so that we can all go together? I'm sure my Mum would love to have a holiday. But she can't get away.

Come to think of it, this year I won't be going, either. Because, for the first time ever, I'm going to Guide Camp in August, which is so fantastically marvellous I can hardly bear to think about it yet, and I've got to get all kinds of things first, like a kit-bag, and blanket-pins, and a palliasse cover to fill with straw when we arrive.

Once I start going to camp, will I ever go on holiday with Granpie again?

It's the same about Saturdays. I don't *want* them to stop, but . . . but now that it's getting to be summery weather, there's sometimes a hike on a Saturday, or wide-games on the Common - though that's not so easy now they're building the big air-raid shelter - and I'd hate to miss any of it.

195

I wish I could be in two places at once.

That's a potty thought. What I really wish is that I could come to Acton on a weekday instead of having to go to my stupid waste-of-time school. Can you *believe* it, we're *still* doing those silly equation drawings in algebra . . . on and on for months, and not getting anywhere. And in English we've stopped parsing sentences and all we do is things like debates and mock-trials, which are maybe a good idea but so far they've been what my Dad calls a Total Wash-Out.

It's forty winks time at the moment and I wouldn't normally be up here at all, but Granpie said to run along and play, as he needed a little extra snooze. However, this wasn't really true. He just wanted me out of the way so that I wouldn't see him studying the newspaper with a worried frown.

I know, because I heard the rustle of him unfolding it as I shut the door. People are always reading the paper with a worried frown these days, and listening to the News all the time, because they think there's going to be a war.

No matter what it is . . . funerals, or wars, or whatever . . . Granpie is very kind and always trying to protect me from knowing about them, as I explained.

I just wish he wouldn't.

I'm not actually interested in all that grown-up stuff, but I *hate* having to kid him along that I don't *know*. Which is daft, considering we've been fitted with our gas-masks, with all that breathe-in-to-make-sure-it-doesn't-fall-off-your-face business, and have them stacked away in the Dining Room cupboard in their cardboard boxes, together with the stuff all ready to stick criss-cross on the windows, just in case.

Anyway, when he said, "Run along now, and play for a minute," I asked if I could come up to his Study. What I wanted to do, was have a good look at the globe of the world that sits on its own stool in the corner. But once I got up here I started looking at all the other things, the boats and the beam-engine and the trip-hammer, and Granpie's model of the Planets going round the Sun, and a beautiful polished flute unscrewed into sections and lying in a box lined with blue silk, and his old fiddle in its case propped up in a corner, and his preaching gown hanging behind the door.

Suddenly, everything had a sort of yesterday-feel, and I wished I was somewhere else.

But once he's finished the paper and we start doing things together, it'll be all right again. And that lovely, exciting, being-over-at-Granpie's-on-a-Saturday feeling will come back.

6

LEAD AND TOFFEE AND THINGS

The soldier stares at his own image in the trembling surface of
the silver lake . . . then droops, collapses, falls and sinks into
oblivion, to be known no more . . . while on the evening air
there rises up the hot, rich smell of burning paint and fiery, clean,
exciting scent of molten metal . . .

Hmmm.

You can't really do a good poetry-think about melting down
one-legged guardsmen. Not unless you pretend they're real, and
go on about their poor faces slithering into the morass, their
busbies slowly sliding sideways until they're only a black scum
on the surface.

Anyway, it isn't evening, it's after lunch.

Mrs Liddington has gone, Aunt M's working upstairs in her
room, the sunny day has gone cloudy, Granpie's finished his
extra-forty-winks, and he and I are melting lead in the Kitchen.

Lead is like Plasticine, in the sense that if you've made an interesting model out of Plasticine, then next week you can roll it up and make something else. When we're melting lead we start by melting down the squiggly shapes we made last time, to remake into a different shape, and only add a soldier if one happens to have bitten the dust. However careful you are, just now and then there's a broken neck which you mend with a bit of match stick but it always looks wobbly, or a broken leg that you fix the same way and bed the bottom of the match in Plasticine moulded round the boot on the stand. But if he breaks another leg, that's him for the ladle.

The ladle is of heavy grey metal with a long handle. We take it down off its hook by the cooker and sit it on the gas ring. Granpie holds the handle while I pop in last time's lead shapes and then light the gas. The silvery pieces are thin and flat, for a reason I'll explain in a minute. Many are too big to lie down, and only a corner of them touches the bottom of the ladle.

We keep quiet, and watch.

It's like watching a strange, live thing. You can't tell when it will start to move.

Granpie says, "Keep your eyes peeled!" and I stand ready with a clean piece of stick in case it gets top-heavy and wants to fall over the edge.

Slowly, slowly, the corner melts and collapses. Silently, snakily, the rest of it sits down on itself, bit by bit, and slides into the pool and becomes a shining lake, pure and shivery and rounded at the edges, like quicksilver.

"Right then, in he goes!" says Granpie.

I've taken out the matchstick and cleaned off the Plasticine. It's a guardsman, like I said, and he's still got one leg but he looks an awful peg-leggy mess and we've decided to sacrifice him. I hold him by the stand and lower him in face downwards so as not to see his eyes, and very, very carefully, so as not to splash, because it's dangerous stuff.

A corner of his stand sticks up out of the lake and is the last to melt. I was going to say 'like a shark's fin', because it's that shape, but really it only looks like what it is, a dark green triangle with the remains of his poor old boot on it, poking up out of a wrinkled bog of red and black and brown and green paint. I float the scum to one side with my stick, and lift it off onto the old tin plate we keep just for jobs like that and carry on scumming until it's a perfect shimmering silver again.

Then Granpie says, "Stand back!" and very slowly, one foot at a time, and steady it . . . another foot, and steady it . . . he goes through the Kitchen with the ladle held out in front of him, and out of the opened back door, and into the yard. He won't allow me to hold the ladle at all. One of my jobs has been to water the yard earlier on with the watering can and sweep it with the hard broom to get rid of every speck of dust, just ready for this moment.

"Now then, here goes!" he says, and tips the ladle with a sort of quick, magic twist. The liquid lead jumps into the air, leaping and shining, and before you know where you are it has stopped moving and is lying on the concrete, quite still, in all kinds of squirly shapes and a few interesting trickles and blobs, like dribbled icing sugar. We walk round them, waiting for them to cool, seeing what we can see from different angles.

This time there's one like a duck with its beak open, and a little bubble in the lead for its eye. Another is a bit like a dragon, or if you turn it round and think again it's maybe a kite with a tail. But my favourite is not very big, about the size of a half-crown, a beautiful smooth shape with rounded curves and little sticky-out bits here and there like a nose, or a chin, so that you can see different faces in it.

You can only tell which you like best when you pick them up, when you feel the thin flatness of them, and smooth the silvery top with your finger.

I think I'll keep the face-shape one in my pencil-box for a while, so that I can look at it in school. The only pity is that it doesn't keep the bright shiningness that it had when it was molten in the ladle. But it's still silky smooth.

Granpie and I tried making a sand mould and pouring the lead into it, to make a bridge for the clockwork train set. The cast came out all right, but it was so rough and pitted from the sand that it wasn't worth the bother.

"The game's not worth the candle," said Granpie, and we melted it down next time to make shapes in the yard.

Granpie's is another L-shaped house, only unlike ours it has the Drawing Room in the long bit of the L and the Kitchen in the short bit. So there's quite a decent-sized yard outside the Kitchen, and an outside WC as well, which is useful if you're in the garden.

It also saves Acton Grannie going up the stairs too often. If it's raining, for instance, and she's been to the upstairs one and is coming down again, she stands at the very top to feel for the banisters with her left hand, and slides her right hand down the wall, and shuffles down very slowly, sort of dot-and-carry.

So Granpie's yard, although not beautiful, is a handy place to have and is also my best place for playing catch-and-clap-and-twist with a tennis-ball against the wall, because there are no boarders having naps on the other side, so I'm not being a Bother.

I expect you know what I mean by catch-and-clap-and-twist. It's the one where you throw the ball against the wall and catch it, but in between the throw and the catch you do first one clap, then three, then five, then twizzle your arms round, then spin your whole self round, and then a throw under your leg. But you do each part five times or ten times or however many times you tell yourself you're going to do. If you drop the ball you have to go back to the beginning and start again. And if you get too good at it you can make it more complicated by adding more claps, or doing two spins.

Once you start doing it you don't want to stop.

But it's peaceful.

You only do it with a little bit of your brain, so there's plenty of room left for thoughts to think themselves.

Sometimes the thoughts just drift in and out again, like all this war-and-Chamberlain-and-Hitler talk that I can't puzzle out because I don't understand it, and the maybe-evacuating-children-to-the-country talk, and Dig For Victory posters all over the place, and Mr and Mrs Meredith next door having an Anderson shelter down the bottom of their garden where our hens lay away.

But more often the drifting-in-and-out thoughts are a whole lot more interesting, about what we did at Guides the night before. Because now the evenings are lighter we're usually out on the bits of the Common that aren't being dug, signalling over a 100 yards distance, or measuring the height of a tree by sighting along a pencil, like in Art, with your thumb at the base of the tree and the pencil point at the top, and then turning the pencil horizontal and having your partner pace the distance from the bottom of the tree until you sight them through the pencil point and shout them to stop, and that's the height of the tree.

However, I'm not playing catch-and-clap-and-twist at the moment.

We've got the glue-pot down off the shelf ready to start the lovely stinky smelly business on the gas ring. Granpie's in the shed sorting out some wood that he'd going to saw and glue to mend a cupboard with. And I'm getting something special ready to glue for Guides, that I'll tell you about in a minute.

We hadn't planned to do gluing, but you know how it is . . . when you finish one job it gives you an idea for the next one. So when Granpie and I went back to the gas stove to clean the tin plate and put it and the lead-melting ladle away, he said, "How about getting the glue-pot on the go?" It might just as likely have been, "Let's make some toffee, shall we? What sort shall it be?" and I'll choose whether it's to be Everton or Old English.

Everton Toffee is soft enough to cut into squares when it's cooled, but Old English you leave to harden on the buttered toffee-tray and then attack it with the toffee-hammer. Sometimes it breaks cleanly along the marks we've made, but there are always plenty of interesting jaggy pieces, and left-over slivers and splinters like black-treacle-coloured icicles, all tangy tasting. We know what it's going to taste like earlier than that, of course, from picking out the fascinating twizzly-shaped blobs of soft toffee lying in the cup of cold water, where we've dropped drips off the spoon to test and see whether it's done.

Anyway, about the gluing . . .

Which reminds me, every time I see Granpie's dear old rusty glue-pot, with its bottom part for the water to boil and melt the bits of hoof-and-hide glue that Granpie buys from Woollie's in a little paper bag, and the top part that we stir the glue in, only you have to put a bit of matchstick between the edges of the two parts, otherwise the water boils over, and it's quite beautifully steamy and messy and stinky enough without that . . . every time I see it I can't help thinking about my mother's work-box.

This work-box is special, because it is the same one that used to be Devonshire Grannie's, and that my mother had counted, "One, two, three, four, five, Mother's Thimble!" in. When I was little, this work-box was never used much, even by Devonshire

Grannie when she was alive, because not only was the inside tray lop-sided and wobbly, but the lid was really badly smashed at the back, just in an awkward place by one of the hinges.

Then years ago when I was eight and couldn't think what to get for my Mum's birthday, I got this idea, and Granpie helped me to sneak the work-box over to Acton, and we mended it. He let me do every little bit myself, and it took lots of Saturdays, because you had to glue one small piece, leave it to harden, and next week glue the next piece, and so on. And there were four little corner pillars to saw and glue in position to sit the inside tray on.

When it was done, Granpie put a bit of his money into the kitty and between us we fitted it out with new reels of coloured cottons all along the back, as well as books of needles and pins. It looked so lovely, it made you almost want to cry . . . well, you know what I mean . . . because it had been done-for, and now it was all right again. My Mum must have felt the same, for tears came into her eyes and she didn't know what to say, for happiness.

This thing I'm getting ready to glue for Guides. It was just an idea that came into my head when Granpie said he had this cupboard to mend. I'd seen a nice rectangular piece of plywood in his shed, about twelve inches by nine, and he let me have it and hunted out a length of thin cord for me. I'm going to have a go at making a Knot Chart for our Patrol Corner.

I haven't asked, but even if they don't want it, it'll be fun to make, with real knots glued onto the wood and their names painted underneath, and the whole lot varnished.

Once the glue is dry, I can do the rest of it at home with my water-colours and the little tin of Copal Varnish I've got left over from making a thumb-stick. My Mum lets me do those jobs in my room, which is still the Room Next to the Tank Cupboard, though I don't know for how long.

With any luck it might be ready for Guides next Friday.

Anyway, I've nearly finished tying the knots . . . Bowline, Sheet Bend, Sheepshank and all the rest, and . . .

Oh, my goodness!

I was going to tell you more about it, and about tying the Hitches round real little bits of wood, and what the glue looks like while it's melting, and how the smell stays in your nose for ages afterwards, and all sorts of things, but . . .

I've just remembered what tomorrow is.

It's the first Sunday in the month, which means Church Parade!

Auntie Marjorie telling me about the dentist on Saturday made me shove next week out of my head, so as to forget, but talking about Guides has made me remember.

And it is such a marvellous thought that I don't know how to tell you.

The Divisional Church Parade, that I told you about, is different, because it is all Guides, and a special service.

Company Church Parade means it's just us going to an ordinary service in the Parish Church. We march there, and the Colour Party takes our flags up to the altar. Apart from that, for anyone who is C of E it is just normal, I suppose.

But . . .

Oh, but!

Each time I go is as marvellous as the first, and is still strange, and Mary who sits next to me has to show me the place in the Prayer Book and I copy her, to know when to kneel and stand and sit. But most of the time I feel I'm in a sort of daze.

Only, how to explain?

I told you what it's like where I go with Granpie, which is not the Congregational church but the same one the Prophets of the Groves go to, as it happens, because it's nearer. Well, it's still the same. There's nowhere for your eyes to look, and the words sort of batter on and on without saying anything special.

But where we go with the Guides is very old, all dark wood like the timbers of a boat, and the ribs of a boat up in the roof, and in between the ribs is painted dull, deep, dark blue and spangled with faint far-away-looking stars. The floor has old flat grave-stones in it, with ancient names worn smooth of people long ago. The light comes through the stained-glass windows in pools of red and blue. And the altar end is deep and mysterious, and when you look at it your eyes go on and on.

And then we sing this thing called the Te Deum.

I *wish* I could explain properly.

It's as if, for the first time in my life, something was telling me what it's all about.

For one thing, it's got this ALL feeling . . . it keeps saying,

'ALL the earth', and 'ALL Angels' and 'Heaven and earth are FULL' . . . like great arms stretching out to gather it all up so that everything belongs together, and the music shouts for joy so that your heart nearly bursts. And the amazing thing is, it's not just *us* singing it, but all the earth, the trees and creatures, and people who've sung it before us, and the ones we are singing about . . . the glorious company of the Apostles, the goodly fellowship of the Prophets, and all the rest of them . . . we're all praising together, and crying out together and belonging together.

Another thing is, it's like Jacob's ladder that went all the way from his stony pillow to Heaven with angels ascending and descending. This Te Deum, it's like that, joining Heaven and Earth so that you can't separate them. It starts off with the Heavens and all the Powers therein, and Cherubin and Seraphin. And right at the end it comes down to 'day to day', and 'keep us this day', and 'in Thee have I trusted'. Only, not separate. It's as if we're in Heaven with them, sharing what they're doing, and they're down here on Earth with us, keeping us company.

Well, that's how I feel about it, anyway.

And . . . it's Church Parade tomorrow!

Which is a whole lot more wonderful to think about than school all next week and the Dreaded Mr Dixon on Saturday.

7

EVEN A LITTLE GARDEN IS GOOD

Tadpoles, snails and plantain leaves . . . dandelion clocks and honey-taste of clover heads . . . grass to chew and beetles to watch . . . I'm just so glad to be in a garden again, Granpie's garden, with time to think and let everything settle down and stop happening.

It's only a week since I was at Mr Dixon's but it feels ages, my brain's whizzing with all the things that have been going on and . . . oh, I don't know, it's just that I feel there hasn't been a minute to sort it all out, and now, at last, I can.

Actually, I want very much to tell you about Granpie's garden, because although it's only the size of a pocket-handkerchief, it's far more full of surprising things than ours is at home. But that'll have to wait till my mind has stopped spinning.

Also, I need to remember it all. There's been so much, it'd be easy to forget.

There are traffic sounds coming distant from over the wall, and Mrs Liddington sounds floating from the Kitchen, and Granpie's whirring the treadle lathe in the shed. In a moment I'll go and help him, but there's no hurry.

If I fiddle around out here for a bit in the sun and the breeze, and pull a few weeds and check the tadpoles, things will pop into my head and sort themselves out.

Well, last Saturday Mr Dixon was as horrible as ever, and Aunt M and I had our swim and came back here for tea. But it was a very strange tea. Although Granpie listened to us telling about my two huge fillings, and how many lengths we'd swum side-stroke, and that sort of thing, he didn't seem to be taking it in. And as we finished he hrmmphed into his beard, put down his napkin and looked at me.

"It's straight home now, I'm afraid," he said, "and I'm coming with you."

He sounded so stern, and didn't smile.

I sort of quavered, "W - why, Granpie?"

"There are things", he said in the strict voice that means you can't ask any more, "that I have to discuss with your Mother."

All the way back in the trolley bus I kept wondering what on earth I'd done wrong, or whether it was something terrible like having to have all my teeth out, or what. Granpie seemed so unnatural. Sometimes he was miles away, and sometimes he shot questions at me out of the blue, about school and things, just filling up gaps in the silence.

I was glad to get home, and into the Kitchen, and get a hug from my Mum.

Luckily it was soup and cold for the boarders that evening and she left me to stir the pot and set out the salad while she went into the empty Dining Room with Granpie. They were in there about a quarter of an hour when I heard the front door shut and my mother came back to me and started dishing up the meal, looking flustered but pleased.

She smiled, and said, "I'll tell you afterwards . . . something quite nice, we hope. Go and ring the gong now, my darling!"

"Well now," she said later when there was time to talk properly, "you know children are being evacuated . . . "

I felt a black hole starting to open up, because I don't want to be sent away.

" . . . and your school is moving to the country - quite soon, in

207

fact, and . . . "

"Oh Mummy, *no!*" I started, but she shushed me and gave me a hug.

"That's what we thought! And I believe, and so does Daddy, and Granpie too, that all of us will be just as safe at home. Now, here's what's going to happen . . . it's all such a rush, Granpie only heard from your school yesterday and he's had to act fast . . . he has made arrangements for you to sit the entrance examination for the High School on Monday and . . ."

My eyes were getting rounder and rounder. The High School!

" . . . that just gives us tomorrow afternoon to get you all spruced up. And on Monday I'm to take you up in the bus for ten o'clock and you can make your own way back for lunch and then cycle down to school in the afternoon as usual. How about that, then?"

"Back to school? To my ordinary school? Must I?"

"Well, yes, my darling! Of course! Until Granpie hears how you did in the exam! You could have gone to the County straight away, I expect, but Granpie thinks the High School is the best, so just do as well as you can, that's all we ask. Come on, let's get that washing-up finished or it'll be yon time, and there's Miss Elphin's drink and her hot-water bottle still to do and . . . "

On Sunday . . .

Granpie was cheerful again. We went for a quick round-the-roads walk after church while he gave me a few tips on doing exams and tested me on mental arithmetic and . . .

On Monday . . .

It was like a holiday, stepping it out to the bus-stop with my Mum and then five stages up the hill and down the other side on the top deck, so that she could enjoy the sight of distant hills beyond the houses. I didn't begin to get nervous till we walked up the steps to the big front entrance.

Inside, everything seemed vast - wide flights of stairs, honey-coloured polished wood, big windows, high ceilings, and huge double doors marked 'LIBRARY'. We were taken to the Head's Study and I was so dithery with nervousness that I can't remember anything about it except lightness and a bowl of flowers and a beautiful picture of water and buildings, and my tall mother in her home-made tailored suit of heathery green being greeted by a tall severe-looking person in a plain green jersey and skirt, with a Scottish sound to her voice, and piercing eyes under a bony brow. You could tell that my mother took to her right away, though to me it was like talking to a mountain and I was shaking in my shoes.

Then a lady came, and led me away up five flights of stairs, past corridors full of classes where lessons were going on, to a little room at the very top of the school, and sat me down at a table to do the exam papers. Then I was happy, and forgot everything else, and before I knew it I'd finished and it was time to go home.

Because they were easy, and interesting. There weren't any History or Geography questions, that I was scared I wouldn't know the answers to. Just a sheet of ordinary sums up to long-division and a few simple fractions. And some things like filling in missing words and punctuation, and choosing alternatives. Last of all came the one I liked best, where you had to choose a practical task from a list of things like Baking a Cake, Darning a Sock, Cleaning Shoes etcetera, and write a detailed description of how to do it, starting at the beginning and going through each stage.

I did Mending a Puncture on a Bicycle.

Because I know all about it and there are so many fascinating bits, like how to get the inner-tube out, and putting spit on it or bubbling it in water to find the hole, and sandpapering, and gluing the patch, and dusting with French chalk, and all the business of tyre levers and not pinching the tube when you get it back in.

So I hoped they would like it.

All week at school . . .

I've been in a sort of daze, just hoping and hoping. Because now that I've been inside that big school . . . I know that's where I belong . . . only, what if I didn't pass?

Some of the girls kept chattering on about whether the school is really going to be in a big mansion by a river, and whether they'll get pony riding.

And some have been very quiet, and not looking happy.

209

And two are being evacuated to America.

On Friday, that's yesterday . . .

Granpie was in the Kitchen when I got back from school. All I know is, I came in through the Scullery as usual and slung my hat and satchel on the back of the door and he and my Mum turned to greet me, all smiles. After that I don't remember a thing except that he was gruff and pleased and my mother's voice sounded as if she was singing, and . . . I *passed!*

No more silly-stupid-waste-of-time-and-not-meaning-anything school . . . I'm going to the *High School!* But when?

Once Granpie had hurried off to get the trolley bus back to be with Acton Grannie, I sat down with my Mum at the kitchen table and we had some tea and bread and syrup while she told it all to me again quietly.

Apparently I had done well enough to count as a scholarship pupil, or something like that, so it will help save money and everyone is very pleased.

"But there's still the uniform to buy," she said, and laughed, "and I'm afraid that's just about all you'll be getting for your birthday! But you won't mind too much, will you?"

I said, "I don't mind, truly I don't, but . . . when? It's still a whole fortnight till my birthday!"

"We're going to give it to you in advance!" said my Mum.

So, today, this morning . . .

My Mum and I went down to the shop that does the school out-fitting. It's a good job I'd grown out of my old blazer, as we'd have had an awful time trying to unpick all that white braid round the cuffs and lapels. So we bought a new navy blazer with the red badge, and a red hatband and tie, and a new tunic because they wear the modern straight ones with a V-neck, much nicer than our old square-necked gym slips with box-pleats and a sash. And two new blouses, and some red material to make a regulation shoe-bag, and - for a treat because it's for my birthday - a gorgeous, long, double-knitted, fringed, red High School scarf!

They said they would deliver it all straight away, so my Mum went home and I got the trolley bus over to Acton the way I always do, and Granpie and Acton Grannie had another advance birthday present waiting for me . . . a grown-up-style real-leather satchel! Which I'm going to need. My raggedy old cloth one is too small, anyway.

And the reason it all has to be in advance is . . .

The Head told my mother she would like me to start straight away! Even though it is so near the end of the school year, she said, it would give me a few weeks to settle in and let the strangeness wear off.

So I'm not going back to my silly school *ever!*

Granpie says he'll take my school books back for me and collect my Bible and things from my desk.

And I start at the High School on Monday!

I'm so happy, and dizzy and sick inside with nervousness . . . and that's why I'm very, very glad I'm here in the garden, because everything's been happening so fast all week, and whizzing on and on like a roundabout that you couldn't get off even if you wanted to . . . but - now - it - has - slowed - down - and - stopped.

The tadpoles have nearly all got legs by now, and what I'm checking is to see if any of them have lost their tails and are ready to hop away and be frogs. Granpie and I have been watching them grow ever since we brought the frog spawn from Gunnersbury in a jam-jar. But they're getting overcrowded now, as the pond is only about as big as a dinner-plate.

When you open the French windows from the Drawing Room, what you see first is a very small lawn with green-growing walls on either side and a really frighteningly high red brick wall at the bottom. The wall belongs to the garage on the other side, and is higher than the house, and runs along the bottom of all the gardens in the row.

The next thing you do, I think, is step out onto the grass and look up, and take a big breath, and feel happy. Because you suddenly remember that however high the wall and however small the garden, it doesn't have a roof, and there's the whole of the sky up there. If you want, you can lie on your back on the grass and forget about everything and float away and away with the clouds.

Coming back to the garden, the right-hand green-growing wall is really a wooden fence completely covered in honeysuckle and clematis at the far end, and with a most beautiful old-fashioned rambler rose at the house end. The rose has shiny dark green leaves and masses of scented, creamy blossoms. And below the rambler are loops and spikes of American blackberry which has no thorns and lovely star-shaped leaves, and later in the year we pick juicy berries for tea.

The green-growing wall on the left is trees and shrubs like hawthorn and laburnum and buddleia, that the peacock butterflies love. Between the grass and the trees is a flower-bed with things like Canterbury Bells and Sweet-William and some tall white daisies with thick dark green stems that are a special place for snails . . . huge ones, the biggest I've seen anywhere. I must admit I still like collecting them for Granpie.

I'll tell you what's on the other side of the trees later.

Hang on, though, I'd better tell you now. Because Granpie's coming out of his shed, and I bet I know what for, so there's something I'll have to explain.

On the other side of the row of trees and shrubs is a space between them and the left-hand fence. In places the trees form a shady tunnel, and there are things like ferns and lilies-of-the-valley. But down the middle of the tunnel runs a concrete path that goes all the way from the kitchen yard to Granpie's shed at the left-hand bottom of the garden.

And that's where we run the engines.

"That's the buffer fixed!" says Granpie happily, and shuts the shed door. "How about it, are you game for a run? Which one shall it be?"

"We did Carmarthen Castle last time, so it's the Flying Scotsman's turn," I say, and we go into the Drawing Room and open the old black cabin trunk.

"Right you are then, all hands to the pump!" says Granpie, and we heave up the tray of railway tracks and carry it into the garden. He doesn't take the locomotive out until we're ready, in case Grannie comes through and trips over it.

We set up the track under the green tunnel of the trees. The engines have proper swively bogey-wheels in front like the real ones, and good enough to take curves, but there isn't room to lay anything but a straight track.

So the actual running of it - with the sun glinting through the leaves onto the brass and dark green paint, and white wisps streaming back from the smoke-stack - is over very quickly.

But setting it up is fascinating.

I put little bits of coal in the tender - not that she burns coal but you can hardly send her along empty - while Granpie puts water in the boiler, then fetches the meths bottle and soaks the cotton-wool in each of the burners, puts the bottle away safely before he lights them, and then lets me hold the handle of the burner-set and push it into the fire box, like the fireman shovelling coal on a real engine.

Then we wait, and watch, and let our minds go small . . . till we seem the same size, and the cab gets big . . . and we are the engine-driver watching the gauges and waiting for the hissing of steam from the safety-valve, and the pressure building up . . . and we turn the handle in the cab, the real little handle in Granpie's Flying Scotsman, and make the whistle blow 'Whoo-Whoo!' . . . and then the magic moment when the pressure mounts, the pistons move all by themselves, the wheels start to turn and gather speed . . . and she's off!

Not very fast . . . but fast enough to enjoy. Otherwise she'd go past in a blur of light and be through the buffers and end up in the Kitchen.

Granpie loves it.

But he needs someone like me to do it for, or he'd feel silly.

It's the same with things like his water-wheel.

The water-wheel is just one little part of a whole watercourse system that Granpie has made. The tadpole pond in the middle of the lawn is fed by a stream that comes from higher up in the right-hand flower-bed. The water for the stream comes from a big square biscuit-tin raised up on bricks. And Granpie has fixed a little tap near the bottom of the tin, so that we can turn the tap on and let out however much water the pond needs.

You can't let out too much at a time when there are tadpoles or you'd float them all away. But at other times you can send down a good swoosh of water and watch the water-wheel half-way down the stream, birling round with a clacking sound and scattering drops into the sun.

Every part of it is very small. It has to be, because you can cross the lawn in three strides. But when everything is miniature, you can imagine it big. You can even, sometimes, imagine that it's real, and not made of concrete. Because the pond has some duck-weed growing, and small rushes, and the stream is fringed with ferns, and the bricks and the biscuit-tin are disguised with rocks to look a bit like a cliff.

We had a lot of fun making it.

But especially Granpie, because he has all week, and I've only got Saturdays.

So he is always thinking up something new. Like the one he's making just now, which is a lighthouse to stand on the biscuit-tin-cliff, with a flashing light worked by battery. He does a little bit at a time, working away in his shed.

A shed is a great place. I wish we had one at home, but my Dad's hopeless with tools, though good with chickens, so we only have the chicken house. And Granpie's shed is special because of the lathe, that he lets me use to make shapes with wood. You have to centre the piece of wood with the centring tool, fix the wood in the jaws of the lathe, choose a cutting tool and fit it into the chuck. Then you stand in front of the lathe, working the treadle with your right foot. The treadle turns a big wheel, the wheel turns the flat leather strap and the strap turns the lathe and your piece of wood whizzes round faster than you can see. You move the chuck further in, a little and a little, till the tool bites the wood, the sawdust flies out, you move the chuck to the right or left, or bring it out and make a new cut further along, and soon you have a turned piece of wood like a banister or a chair leg.

That is, if you're patient, which I'm not . . . well not very.

"Gently does it!" says Granpie. "That's the ticket!"

Or he says, "If at first you don't succeed, try, try, try again!"

It takes a lot of experimenting to know which cutting tool is best for the job, and how much pressure to use, and how thin you can dare to make a ring without it breaking. I'm not much good at it, but it's still a lovely feeling, working away in the gloom of the shed with the smells of oil and turps and wood, the light coming in the open door and nobody to bother you.

*　　*　　*　　*

214

There are all these things to do, and all Acton Grannie can do is sit. It must be awful.

But she does like to sit in the garden in the sun, and feel the breeze and listen to the birds, and that's why Granpie has built her a little summer-house at the far end, up against the high brick wall and next to a sycamore tree that seeded itself there.

If the grass is damp she prefers to sit on a dining chair on the little concrete strip outside the Drawing Room, but on dry and warm days Granpie and I help her negotiate over the tussocky bits and between the flower-bed and the pond until she's safely at the summer-house. It's quite a pretty summer-house, painted green and with transparent pretend-stained-glass paper that Granpie has stuck on the inside of the windows, but to tell the truth it's so small and stuffy inside that it's mostly useful for keeping the deckchairs in, and Grannie can't sit in a deckchair, anyway.

Even so, she enjoys it at the summer-house. It's nice and sheltered and we bring an upright chair down and have it ready so that we can sort of lower her onto it when we get her down the garden. Because she really is quite heavy. But it's a nice family feeling, having her out there with us, even though she never says very much except things like, "Oh, just hark at that blackbird!" or, "Are the roses out yet?"

So I sit by her for a bit and say what I can see, and answer her questions, or bring her a flower to feel, or see if I can find any of last year's sycamore seed-wings and throw them into the air one at a time and tell her how each one gets on. If they're not too old and broken up they twizzle down like little propellers, and some come down straight and some drift off sideways and go quite a long way.

So there's always something new to tell her, and next week there'll be a whole lot more.

I hardly dare think about Monday, and my new school. All I know is, it's so big and so different from my other schools that there's no picture in my mind to tell me what it'll be like. So although I'm longing for it, I'm all hollow and fluttery-feeling inside, as if I was going to jump off a cliff and fly.

It's a good job there's plenty to do. I'm going to mow the grass next, I think, after we've finished with the engines. And then it'll be tea-time, and then maybe we'll have a game of chess, and perhaps have another go at the home-made jigsaw puzzle we're making with the fretsaw, which is fiddly but fascinating.

I wonder what it's like being Acton Grannie, and not having jobs to do or even school to look forward to. She likes to hear all about school and asks me lots of questions about it, but I've never asked her about when she was at school. I wonder if she can remember. I'll have to ask her.

I suppose there are lots of things she could tell me if I asked her. But somehow there never seems to be time.

8

THE WRONG HOUSE

The big trees beside the road are bending and swooshing and I wish I could let my hair fly free in the wind, but I'm cycling to school and it's my first day so I'd better behave. My hat with the new red hatband is gripped on tight with elastic and my new satchel is sitting solid between my shoulder-blades and only bouncing a little bit because there's not much in it yet.

I stand on the pedals and push like mad up the hill and try to keep pace with the red double-decker that's full of girls with red hatbands and red ties.

If they look out, they'll wonder who I am, but I can't keep up.

Then the top of the hill and round the corner and it's like flying, whizzing down the other side and no one can hear me and I shout and sing and it's glorious. Like being part of the sky and the clouds and the trees bending and the leaves blowing . . . and like being really, truly *me* and yet not me but part of everything, and you sit high on your bike and fly through the sky and you have to shout because of the glory.

Then I've caught up with the bus because it's stopped at the

k

school gates and a crowd of them is pouring out. Suddenly I'm not even really me any more. Just a shy awkward person who doesn't know where to go and doesn't know anybody, and all gone to jelly inside. And everyone is nice but they all talk at once to each other and swing tennis rackets, and I haven't got one and I'm hopeless at tennis, anyway.

But there are lots of cyclists. I follow them, park my bike in the racks, open the saddle-bag, pull out my new red shoe-bag with my gym shoes in, and follow the crowd into the cloakrooms.

They're huge! You could get lost here! A forest of shiny black pegs and red bags with people's names embroidered on in white, and benches underneath and sort of cages to put your outdoor shoes in . . . a sea of legs and arms and blazers and satchels, and tossing waves of hats leaping up and hair being combed, and laughing and talking and shouting faces that you could drown in and never come up. And everyone knows everyone else, and as far as size goes, I'm big, but I feel very small and creep along quietly so as not to get noticed, until I find a teacher to ask and she tells me my peg number and points out which row.

Once I've got a peg number, everything calms down and faces turn into people. Because the girl at the next peg says, "You're new! What's your name? It's all right, we're in the same class - I'll show you!"

And she takes me in tow, up to the classroom for Register, and filing down in twos all hushed for Assembly, and chattering back up the stairs, swinging round the corners and up again . . . and down again and round again and up again . . . to the Art Room and the Physics Lab, to Maths and Geography and English . . . up again and round again and down again . . .

At the end of the day I'm whirling and in a daze. I've loved every minute. And that is definitely and absolutely all I can say.

That was three weeks ago, and school is finished for the summer holidays, so by now I ought to be able to tell you a lot more about it. And of course I could, but there's not much point in going on about it, except to say that:

1. I love it, and it's a proper school, and has all the things
   and teachers and equipment that a proper school should

have, like the labs with bunsen burners and sinks, and the Geography Room with an epidiascope and lots of pictures, and the Gym with ropes and travelling bars and apparatus, and the glorious Art Room with pots and easels and high-up views to the hills.

2. I'm still very new, and it was sort of end-of-termish anyway, so I can't say what it's like usually. When I start all over again in a new year, and we've all moved up a class together, that'll be the proper beginning of it for me.

I could tell you soppy things, of course. Like when I'd just been there a week and came top in Composition, and this silly girl whose name I won't say (we don't have many silly ones but there are a few) said, "Oh, I *am* glad you've come! We're so tired of Felicity always coming top in everything and it makes a change to have someone else!" Phew! I escaped quickly!

Anyway, it was about 'Pets', so probably Miss Macfarlane liked the bits about Tiddles and Marmalade, and about Tigger. Sometimes I wish we could have a dog again.

And there are some special things, but they're not easy to tell because they are more feelings. Like the feeling you get when you go through those high panelled doors marked 'LIBRARY' and tiptoe into that hush, with people quietly reaching down beautiful books of all colours from the tall shelves, and light streaming in from the big windows onto Seniors sitting studying at polished tables and so interested they never even lift their heads, except sometimes to turn a page, or fetch another book, or look out for a moment at the grass of the quadrangle.

Or like the happy feeling that comes when I'm not thinking about it and I wonder why I'm happy. And it's because at last there's somewhere where I belong, and that's going somewhere, and it's all stretching out in front of me, but no hurry.

I've found a new way to cycle to school.

I still like up the hill and down again best. But my alternative route makes a change, especially when it's raining, because it doesn't go high at all but wiggles around by the back roads. Also, it brings you out to the back entrance to the school grounds and that gives you another choice. You can get off your bike and wheel it past all the school tennis courts and across the netball pitches and so on until you come to the cycle racks and the front entrance. Or you can keep cycling and go by the Unadopted Road.

It actually has a street name-plate attached to a wall, saying 'UNADOPTED ROAD', as if that was its name. Which I think is funny but nice, like 'TRESPASSERS WILL' in the Pooh stories. You can certainly see that it's unadopted - that nobody wants it, I mean - because of all the potholes that you have to bump in and out of. But I think it is beautiful, all sand and gravel and ups and downs like a country road, and dark and secret with overgrown trees like a green jungle.

I asked my Dad what the unadopted bit really meant and he explained to me about the Council not having taken it over and all that, and . . .

That reminds me, talking about my Dad. I forgot to say that I've had my birthday.

That must sound funny, saying 'that reminds me', as if a birthday is a thing I'd forget. But actually, I had. Because . . . oh well, never mind . . .

What was I saying? Oh yes, about my Dad. I wasn't expecting any more presents, but he'd bought me a wonderful new proper navy-blue kit-bag for Guide Camp, which is quite soon now, and had painted my name on it with white paint in big block capitals, the way we're supposed to.

That was on Friday. Not yesterday, but the Friday before that. And my Mum had iced a special sponge with my name on and twelve candles, and made a trifle with cherries and angelica and ratafia biscuits on top, and we had it altogether with the boarders in the Dining Room at the evening meal. And I had a nice time, I suppose, but . . .

Oh but . . .

I keep remembering what I don't want to remember.

I'm remembering what happened two Saturdays ago, the first Saturday after I'd started at the High School.

I can forget it for a while but then it comes back.

*   *   *   *

220

It began so happily.

Granpie hadn't seen me all week and he was so longing to hear all about it that he didn't wait for me to come to Acton, but came over to us soon after breakfast. He has never done that before on a Saturday. Anyway, he fixed a wobbly castor on one of the lounge armchairs and tightened loose stair-rod fixings while I helped my Mum clear up and make beds, and then off we went together with plenty of time to talk on the way.

He so much wanted to hear about the High School and I so much wanted to tell him. And I did. The only thing is, you can talk the hind leg off a donkey, the way my Dad is always saying I do, but even if you use millions of words you can't explain what it is you want to explain. Like, if there was an enchanted castle where every step you took felt magic and happy, you'd try in vain to describe it, and end up talking about all the unimportant parts like the turrets and battlements.

So I described all the classrooms, and told him what we'd done that week in Physics and Biology and so on. And I told him things I thought he'd like to hear, how there are two classes in every year called 'A' and 'B', and I'm a 'B', but that doesn't mean we're not as good at the 'A's, because we are, but for Maths we're reshuffled so that there's a top and a bottom class, and I'm in the top one, which is going to be absolutely fantastically marvellous. Because Miss Haynes is little, and old, and bright-eyed and quick, and loves what she's doing, and she goes just as fast and furious as we can keep up. At least I think so, except it's been revision so far, and maybe exams next week.

When we got to Acton, Granpie said, "Now, you stay and tell Grannie all about it while I go up to the shops." Because he hadn't been for the paper and the bread, with coming over to us so early. And I guessed that he wanted to buy something special and secret for tea as well, to celebrate.

So I sat on the sofa and told Grannie lots of it all over again. Not all of it, but more of what she'd want to know, about what the school looks like, and how many in the class and what their names are, and about changing into gym shoes when we get there, and about Assembly, and what we wear for Gym, and that I wear her vests. Which I do, but we keep our blouses on so it's not so bad, but I didn't say that.

After a bit Grannie took her feet off the fender and started pushing herself up out of her chair, saying, "That was nice, but I'll have to go upstairs. You run along and play the piano for a while."

So she shuffled out of the room and up the stairs one at a time, and I went off to the Drawing Room. Granpie was being quite a while but that didn't surprise me because he was probably searching for the something special. And anyway people are always stopping and talking to him for ages, and he gets talking to people, too. Like the time we were in the newsagent's buying me some stamps for my album and there was a young man doing the same thing and Granpie started talking and discovered that his name was Count Boris Vladimir de Minkwitz, and Granpie was so excited to have met a real White Russian Count that he invited him to tea the next week, to swap stamps with me.

Oh dear, I don't really want to tell about this. But it's no use putting it off . . . I can't not tell you, so I'll get it over with quickly.

I'd played two pieces when there was the most terrible awful terrifying noise I've ever heard, as if a chimney was falling through the roof.

It was loud, and horrifying, and full of fear. Rumble-rumble-bump-bump-bump-crunch. Frozen silence. Then Mrs Liddington running and me running, and Acton Grannie like a heap of old clothes jammed against the wall at the bottom of the steep straight part of the stairs, beginning to moan.

Then Mrs Liddington is crying out to me in a terrible voice, "Run and fetch help! Quickly!" and I am running out of the house and across the pavement and out into the road with my hands up to my head and calling out, "Oh, come! Oh, come! Oh, come!" and I'm going on standing there in the middle of an empty street, looking wildly all around and crying, "Oh, come - come - come!" in this dreadful sobbing, groaning sort of shout that is tearing up from my insides.

Then people are running to me, and running in through the open door, and I don't know any more until I find myself in a strange house. It has the same sort of bow-window as Granpie's and a woman sits me down at the window and tells me to watch for Granpie coming, and then she goes away.

I sit there and never take my eyes from the street. I can't think and I can't feel. Some part of me down deep is going, "Poor Grannie - poor Grannie - poor Grannie . . . " on and on and on, but I can't think about what has happened, or is happening or will happen. I'm just blank.

It's as if I've stopped living.

But when Granpie comes, it will be all right.

So I keep watching.

Then I see him. He's walking so fast that he's leaning forward, his head is pushed forwards from his hunchy shoulders and his eyes are staring straight ahead. He hasn't seen me. He doesn't know I'm here! He is going past!

I shout with a huge voice, "Gra - anpie!"

His face turns, his eyes don't seem to know me and he never slackens his terrible hurrying pace. His mouth says, "You're in the wrong house," without any tone in his voice, or any surprise, as if it is of no interest to him at all. His face turns away and he is gone.

I go on sitting.

I'm in the wrong house, but there's nothing I can do about it.

If I tell you that everything came all right again quite quickly, you'll think I am awfully callous. And in any case it's not true, because it didn't come all right for Acton Grannie. She had broken her hip, and I don't know whether she had hurt her head as well, or whether it was her heart, because grown-ups don't tell you all these things, but she died in hospital the next day. And I was very sorry. It was a truly horrible thing to happen.

But I'd rather not talk about it, because I suppose I'm a bit ashamed at not feeling more deeply about it, but it's no use pretending. Except, I'm sorry for Granpie.

Also, I'm ashamed of myself running out in a panic like that. Twelve years old, and I'm a Guide and supposed to Be Prepared! I don't like to think about it, and I don't like to think what a baby I was, expecting Granpie to be thinking about *me*, when he was hurrying to get to Grannie.

Once I got home and had a bit of a cry and talked with my Mum, I understood everything and, to tell you the truth, got over it in two shakes of a duck's tail and was back to school on the

223

Monday, and the last two weeks have been so busy and happy with lessons and games and singing, and Guides, and practising doing lashings for making camp furniture, and helping Mum make my palliasse cover and all sorts of other things, that I haven't thought about Grannie very much. Nor about Granpie an awful lot either, to tell the truth.

There's so much to fit in, and never enough *time!*

And I didn't see Granpie last weekend, anyway, because we were to let him be on his own to be quiet.

However, last night was the end-of-term concert and prize-giving (not for me, as I'm too new for prizes), and the whole school sang *Let Us Now Praise Famous Men*, which we've been practising. There's that bit at the end that goes all quiet and then works up to a big crescendo:

> 'And some there be which have no memorial,
> Who are buried as though they had never been.
> Their bodies are buried in peace,
> But their name - liveth - for e-e-e-ever more!'

I thought about Acton Grannie then. And Devonshire Grannie, and Miss Fazackerly. But not for long.

And then I felt a bit uncomfortable. Because I hadn't seen Granpie since Grannie fell, and the next day I was going to Acton again.

But now I'm here it's all right. Granpie is still Granpie. And it's Granpie and me the same as usual, only a bit quieter.

After lunch we didn't stay in the house but walked to Gunnersbury Park and fed the ducks and things like that. And Granpie didn't talk about what had happened, so I couldn't either, because the words get stuck and won't come past your teeth.

However, he was doing his whistling under his breath, all the time we were walking. Come to think of it, I should say 'with his breath', not 'under it', because it makes no difference whether he is breathing out or breathing in, the tune keeps on going just the same, only very soft, like part of the breath. And what he was whistle-breathing today was the hymn that goes:

> 'Through the night of doubt and sorrow
> Onward goes the pilgrim band,
> Singing songs of expectation,
> Marching to the Promised Land.'

Which was one that Grannie liked, because there's a lot in it about light, and chasing far the gloom and terror. So I knew he was thinking about her.

But then there was an unusual sound, the heavy sound of aeroplanes high above, and he stopped whistling and looked up.

"Bombers?" he muttered to himself. And after a bit he gave a little sighing breath and muttered again, just a whisper, "Maybe it was a mercy."

But after we'd fed the ducks and had an ice-cream he cheered up a lot and said, "Come on, let's see if the Museum is still open!" and it was, and we went in and looked at the penny-farthing and the boneshaker and the carriages that we've seen plenty of times before.

When I saw the carriage that's called a landau, my mouth opened all by itself, without my meaning it to, and said, "Do you remember . . ."

Then I shut it and didn't say any more, but Granpie looked at me and smiled, and said, "Yes! The buttercup fields!"

And we talked happily about Acton Grannie's special once-a-year outing. It was her choice. She never wanted to go anywhere else, only to the buttercup fields that used to be on Western Avenue before the Hoover factory came. We all used to go, my mother and father and little brother and Acton Grannie and Granpie and me, riding along like royalty, pulled by two horses, in the open carriage that used to stand among the square black taxis on the taxi rank. But not for some years now.

It was a lovely, summery thing to do. A tradition. Grannie's country drive.

"Yes," said Granpie in a comfortable voice, as we came out from the museum and walked past the lily pond. "Your Grannie always loved the buttercup fields, even though we had to see them for her."

And then he did a little hrrmph into his pointy beard, and said huskily, "I'm glad you remembered."

225

9

THE END OF THE HOLIDAYS

It's nearly the end of the summer and a strange new sound is heard in our boarding-house.

A musical sound, but vague, and unlike anything our grand piano has ever played in its life, of hands rippling up and down the keyboard in a shapeless sort of way, or galloping fiercely on the spot like horses champing at the bit.

It's a new boarder called Mr Spry playing Rachmaninov and his own compositions. His music follows us round the house and floats out into the garden.

It's the hottest summer anyone can ever remember. The French windows are standing wide open to catch some breeze, and the vague music wafts out over the dry ferns in the rockery. It floats on over the worn-out grass and the deckchairs under the may tree and the chickens churrking away contentedly and having dust baths down the bottom. Perhaps they like it, because they're producing lots of eggs. Which is very helpful of them, because what my mother is keenest on just now is stowing away stacks of food for the winter, on account of this probably-going-to-be-a-war-

226

and-food-rationing stuff they all keep talking about.

So the music is like a sound-picture of us at the moment . . . sometimes faint and feeble like the old ladies and sometimes fast and furious like my Mum and Kitty Carter and me in the kitchen.

Mrs Ritchie and Miss Elphin keep indoors in the shade. Miss Elphin folds her knitting pattern in half and waves it in front of her face. But Mrs Ritchie rummaged in her chest-of-drawers and underneath her best black lace shawl and her spare combinations she found a beautiful ebony and ivory fan from the old days when she used to go dancing, and she wafts it around elegantly with a naughty smile and totters across the Hall to listen to Mr Spry.

But in the Kitchen we've been going at it non-stop, boiling jam, bottling plums and greengages in Kilner jars in the oven, salting down runner beans, and making galvanised buckets-full of eggs preserved in horrible isinglass like poisonous-looking snow. My Mum does the eggs, not me. But I've seen more runner beans this year than I'd care to mention, and after a bit you get pretty fed up with stringing them and slicing them and putting them into jars with salt in between the layers.

At the same time we've been full-steam-ahead with the blanket wash, with great poundings of the dolly-tub and churnings around of the mangle handle, and getting red in the face with the steam, and galloping backwards and forwards between the Scullery and the washing-lines in the garden. Once they've dried in the sun, each one has to have a red wool 'IX' embroidered in the corner (short for '1939') to show the year they got washed.

Then it's back to fruit bottling and searching in the backs of the cupboards for yet another empty brown stone seven pound marmalade jar for yet more runner beans and salt. But after a bit my Mum sends me out of doors to run around or play with my brother.

I can't go over the wall to play with Anna any more because she and her brother have been evacuated to America.

Out in the garden the deckchairs are sitting there looking lonely, collecting bits of leaves and haws, and no one using them.

Sometimes I flop down in one for a bit, only not for long, as it gets pretty boring lying half on your back doing nothing.

But in the long warm evenings when dusk begins to fall and the blackbird is spink-spinking or doing a few thoughtful warbles from the apple tree, my mother slips out for a few moments. She lifts the looping canvas of the deckchair to slide the bits off, and lowers herself down and sinks into quiet.

Sometimes she snatches a few moments earlier in the evening, and Mrs Ritchie comes out too, and they chat, and have a laugh, till my Mum jumps up and says, "Oh, I must go!" And when Miss Hooper comes back from work she often sits out there for a while before the evening meal, and stretches her arms and takes big breaths. She'll smile up at us and say, "It's an improvement on the City!" and then she reads her library book.

I think Miss Hooper's work will be staying put, and she'll go on living with us.

I hope so. I don't like all these changes, there are too many of them. Even our nice greengrocer says he maybe won't be coming much longer, because he has been called up, and the milkman has as well.

Then there's what my Dad would call a question-mark over Mr Sprigget. He's supposed to be still away on holiday, but he came back early two days ago and seems to be spending quite a lot of time in his room doing what sounds like packing. Perhaps his business is moving. I'll get to know eventually.

But worst of all, Mr Grüning has gone. I suppose he has evacuated himself to the country, or to his sister's, but no one says. I don't think he wanted to go. Dear old papery, tobacco-ey Mr Grüning, so brown and thin, I miss him . . . and Kali and Shiva and the Kiplings. I don't even know what Mr Grüning's Room looks like any more, now that Mr Spry has come to live in it. Mr Spry is almost the opposite of Mr Grüning, because instead of being quiet and old-fashioned and painfully polite, Mr Spry is bright and genial and enjoys conversation.

Perhaps that's not the right word, actually. What I mean is, he likes to talk about his music, and asks you to give an opinion on what he's just written. As I don't usually like it, I say something nice but untruthful, and escape quickly. He has grey hair and a pink face, and wears sprightly grey-and-white check suits and a bow-tie. When he's composing he tries out a few notes and chords on the keys and then leans forward and adds them in

228

pencil, very neatly, to his musical score, humming to himself and smiling.

But soon he starts playing again, with the lid of the big concert grand open and propped up, and the vaguely rippling and galloping sounds float out over the garden and around the house.

A sort of fairly peaceful background that you don't have to listen to.

There's another strange new sound in our house, that's less peaceful but a lot more fun . . . yip-yipping and please-play-with-me puppy noises!

Who says wishes don't come true!

I know we said we'd never have another dog, after Tigger died, but sometimes things just happen, and . . .

This was - oh, ages and ages ago, about the beginning of the summer holidays and now it's nearly the end. My Mum and Kitty and I were in the Kitchen, when the door opened just a crack and my Dad's head came round, looking dreadfully apologetic, and he said in a small voice like a little boy who's been naughty, "I couldn't help it!"

And in he came, his arms cradling a bulge in his old sports jacket, and a poky little head looking out . . . a poky little head with huge sleepy eyes and floppy ears. My Dad put him down gently on the Kitchen floor, and it was a tiny greyish-fawn pup with big paws and wobbly legs and a long skinny tail.

Then everything seemed to happen at once. My mother gave a crooning noise, dropped the apple she was peeling and swooped the puppy up into her arms, saying, "Oh . . . Bun!" reproachfully to my father - they've always called each other 'Bun' and 'Bunny' because of the rabbit mugs when they first met - and to me, "Run and fetch a box from the Cupboard Under the Stairs, and an old piece of blanket!" To the pup she said, "Who've we got here, then?" and cuddled him under her apron, and he whimpered and licked her nose, while Kitty Carter made a nice warm rubber hot-water bottle and wrapped it in the blanket, and fed him some warm milk and made him snug in the box in his new home, which is underneath the big dresser next to the pile of newspapers and the tea-chest.

My Mum washed her hands and got back to work, smiling, but

also saying, "Did you really have to?" to my father - because she's got enough to do already - and he sat down with a cup of tea and explained that when he had been coming home on the top of the trolley-bus (he didn't have a rehearsal and he'd been over to Acton) there'd been a man with five Alsatian puppies in a box, so he'd got talking to him and discovered that the man was taking them to the pet shop to sell. He knew they were a bit too young to leave their mother, but he didn't know what else to do, because he had to go off for training or something. When my Dad broke the news to him that the pet shop would be closed because it was Wednesday afternoon, the man began selling them off there and then for half-a-crown each.

So you see he *did* have to. There was nothing else for it, and he really couldn't help it.

"What's his name?" I asked.

My Dad made hmming noises and cogitated, the way he does, and then said hesitantly, "I thought we would call him Skipper ... do you think?"

Skipper he is. And I think he is going to be my best friend.

My Mum said afterwards that she thought at first it was a rat, he was so skinny. He's not skinny now, but a fat and busy pup who likes chewing everything including his lead when I take him out, which he wants me to do all the time except when he flops out and goes to sleep. When he is awake he yips and puppy-growls and tussles and jumps and chews. But when he's getting sleepy he is loving and gentle and cuddly. And almost any time at all he'll wriggle all over when I call him, and roll over to have his tum tickled.

And he has big brown eyes that understand me.

I was thinking.

You know what I said about Skipper going to be my best friend, well I really believe that. I'm shy of saying this, but I feel I do need a friend. And I hope that when I get back to school, there's another new girl, so that I can have a partner. You have to have a partner and keep the same one all the term, for lining up in twos to go to Assembly and change classrooms and things. The school has a junior section and most of the others have been there for ages, so they all had partners already, and no one left over for

230

me. Not that it matters. But it would be nice.

Also, I've put off mentioning school for two reasons. One is that there were all these other things to tell you about. And the other is that I can't help getting so excited about school that it's hard to bother thinking about anything else . . . almost like my real life properly beginning, if that doesn't sound too soppy . . . but that's not the sort of thing you like to tell people when their minds are full up with only one thing, this war-or-maybe-war.

It hasn't happened yet, and everyone hopes it won't and is afraid it probably will. Even if they're not talking about it, you can see that it's in their minds - the grown-ups, I mean - and they're worrying about it all the time.

If I happen to be around when my father has the wireless on for the News I hear bits about it, and talk about Poland, but it's just sort of going on in the background. I can't think about it because I don't understand it and no one explains. Now that she hasn't got Miss Fazackerly's *Daily Telegraph* to borrow, Miss Elphin gets my Dad to fetch her one sometimes, but she doesn't leave it lying around. And Granpie has one, but when I'm over there on a Saturday he only reads it in his forty winks time, and then shoves it away under the cushion and we go and do something else.

So I don't see a newspaper and I don't understand about this war stuff.

And *that* is just about the feeblest excuse I've heard in all my born days! I'm twelve years old, for goodness sake, and I could find out if I wanted to!

It's just that it's hard to be bothered with boring grown-up stuff when there's so little time to fit in all the interesting things I'm busy with, and when I'm not busy - like in bed at night - I think about school . . . about the people, and about how it will be netball next term, which I'm good at if they let me be Goal Defence . . and about starting German, and about Algebra and Geometry which I can't wait to get on with, and how we have proper Biology lessons with Miss Cooper in a white lab coat and how maybe at last we'll get taught how babies are born, which I still can't work out, though I doubt it, as we finished plants' repro-ductive systems last term and she says we're starting this term with the amoeba . . . and about Assembly which, actually, I miss, and I do think about, and might tell you sometime . . .

. . . and when I'm in bed I also think about Skipper, and about

231

his puppy biscuits that I keep in my blazer pocket when I take him out, and share them with him, and about which are his favourites and which are mine . . . and planning ways of training him to heel (only I don't think I will, because he's my friend, and I'd rather have him leaping along beside me) and to stay and fetch . . .

. . . also I think about Guides and plan out what I'm going to do, such as, for instance, I've a sort of shoe-box dolls' house to finish off for my Toymaker Badge and some stories to think up for the Writer's one, not to mention that I'll have to grit my teeth and do the horrible Needlewoman's Badge this winter, because I'll need it for my First-Class . . .

You see? Feeble excuses! I'm at it again!

So . . . what I think is, it's nearly September and I'll be back to school soon with too much on my mind and too much homework, so I'd better get down to it before then. The best thing will be if I do it when I go over to Granpie's this Saturday. I'll ask him, and sit down and have a proper read of his *Daily Telegraph* and see if he'll explain the bits I don't understand.

That reminds me, talking of newspapers, I haven't told you about Guide Camp two weeks ago. It was in Devon, on a cliff top.

The reason newspapers remind me is because of this picture in my mind of our Captain sitting on the beach when we went there in the afternoons . . . she's sitting on the pebbles with her legs stretched out in front of her, leaning forward . . . she's not smiling, she's not watching us run and swim, she's not looking at sea, sky, sun, seagulls, seaweed, sand-flies, shells or anything at all that's there . . . her arms are stretched out sideways, holding *The Times* open as far as it will go, and her face almost buried in the pages so that all I can see is a worried frown under her dark curly hair, and eyes that never look up but scan each word and each line, down each column and up to the top again.

It wasn't a very jolly camp.

Except for camp-fires at night, and singing. That was good.

But a thick white sea-mist came up every morning and blotted out the sun and was damp and chilly. And we always seemed to be rolling up bedding, rolling up the brailing of our bell-tent, hammering tent-pegs, scouring dixies, making camp furniture like wash-basin stands and shoe-racks, and feeling miserable and home-sick and trailing off to the latrines, because the lats are the only place private enough to be miserable in.

Actually, it was only Mary and I who felt home-sick, because we're a bit young. The older Guides, the ones who are about fourteen and fifteen, they all seemed very happy.

I'll come back to that in a minute, but there's something I need to explain first.

Please skip over this bit if you don't want to read it. Only, you see, although life has got so fascinatingly busy and full-up recently that I haven't done very *much* thinking, I have done *some*.

It's just that I'm getting more shy of mentioning it.

But if I'm to be truthful, I can't leave it out, so here goes.

Life is still a puzzle.

Only now it's more *me* that's the puzzle, not other people.

I don't feel quite like the same *me* that I was last year, but I'm not sure why.

What is there different about being twelve, than being eleven? The thing that is supposed to happen to me, hasn't happened yet, so it can't be that.

There is something missing, but I don't know what.

Just to clear the decks, as my Dad says, I can tell you here and now it definitely is *not* boyfriends, as I can't think of a more boring subject. Shirley Jenks at school is always going on about hers, and when I'd only been there a week she asked me if I'd got one. So I said yes. But the only boys I know are the sort who run along the tiles at the Baths and push you in and the ones I was sliding with when I fell through the ice and got steaming legs.

So it's no good making up stories about myself and pretending to be what I'm not. So here goes again, a second time.

I feel a longing and an emptiness that is painful.

And I don't know what it is.

If you are hungry you know you want food and if you're sleepy you know you need sleep, and if you're miserable you want your Mum to give you a cuddle, but it's not like any of these. It hasn't

233

a name . . . it's like the feeling you get when a sunset makes your heart want to burst. Only it's more definite than that . . . like a hole in my life that needs to be filled.

Then when I joined the Guides I thought the Guide Law was it, the thing I was looking for . . .

I don't like saying this because it sounds too pious, but I did *very* much want something to live by, but although the Guide Law will do for now, it isn't enough.

The only thing that sort of fills the hungry hole inside me - stupidly enough to say, I suppose - is Assembly. It's a bit like when the star spoke to me and calmed down the pain and the longing. And I miss it. The prayers and psalms are old, and Assembly is the same every day - every day of the week, never ever different - yet it's new every day.

Once all the classes are in the Hall, hundreds of us sitting in rows on the floor whispering and chattering away, the Prefects file in and sit on chairs at the front, and then a hush falls and we all stand as the Head comes in. She moves down between the rows of us all silent as trees in a forest, walking slowly, steady and tall with measured step, and up onto the platform to look at us under her bony brow and say, "Let us pray," and start with the first prayer, which is often the one that goes, " . . . deliver us when we draw nigh to thee, from coldness of heart and wanderings of mind, that with heart and mind we may worship thee . . ." She doesn't put her feelings into it, just says the words in a calm, plain way.

Then comes the hymn, and then before the Benediction we read a psalm out loud. The Head reads the first verse in her calm Scottish voice and all of us, the whole school speaking together, say the next, and so on turn and turn about. It is pretty special and seems to mean a lot.

Verses stick in your mind and stay with you, like:

    ' . . . then shall all the trees of the wood rejoice
       before the Lord, for he cometh . . .'
and:
    ' . . . there is that leviathan whom thou hast made to
       play therein . . .'
and:
    'What is man, that thou art mindful of him? and the son

of man, that thou visitest him?
For thou hast made him a little lower than the angels,
and hast crowned him with glory and honour.'

Once upon a time I used to say what I felt about marvellous words like that. But now I can't . . . it's too big. Like when you say, 'Bless the Lord, O my soul; and ALL that is within me, bless his holy name . . .'
What is this ALL, that is within me?

To come back to those grown-up Guides at camp.
Often they'd be walking between the tents, laughing and chattering. But one day, three of them were strolling along with their heads together, talking in serious and hushed voices, and then I heard one of them say more loudly, "Oh, but what I really like is going to Early Service very early in the morning when it's hardly light and everything is so still . . . I love that!"
And I burst out, "Oh! So do I!" and caught them up, to walk with them and be part of what they were saying.
But they turned round, startled, as if I were a sneak-thief creeping up on them, and said, "But you're too young! You're not confirmed, are you?"
"No," I said, and hung my head and dropped back.
I don't know what 'confirmed' is, so I suppose I can't be.
They thought I was a cheat, pretending. Why couldn't they understand what I meant? I didn't mean, "I go to Early Service, too," only that, "Oh yes, that's the sort of thing I would like, going out in the still of the morning with the dew on the leaves."
I meant . . . oh, I meant that what they said made me feel at home. As if that, too, is a place where I belong, even though I haven't reached it yet.
But by turning shocked and disapproving faces, they shut me out. I dropped back and left them to their big-girl talk, and went and sat in the lats and howled.
Ho hum . . . aren't I stupid? To howl, I mean.
Perhaps it was just because of leaving my pyjamas on the damp grass one day. I had a temperature and achy legs by the time I got home.
But I'm fine now.

And tomorrow is 'Rabbits, Rabbits!' for the first of September and the day after that is Saturday and Granpie's, and before we know where we are it'll be term-time, and new books and netball and German and . . .

Oh no! Skipper's yowling under the piano. I'll have to go and rescue him.

It's the way Mr Spry's music affects him. Skipper can't resist sneaking in through the French windows to listen, but then he starts thinking he's a baby wolf baying at the moon. If he gets into the habit of it, he'll maybe do it to Mum's singing, and that'd be awful.

So I'm off.

It's Saturday, and I'm not at Acton.

Things are getting very strange.

My mother phoned up yesterday and asked Granpie if he'd mind coming over to us today instead, to help her with some work and have his midday dinner and tea with us. So Mrs Liddington and Auntie Marjorie are managing without him, and he is up the step-ladder fixing heavy curtains and making sure the top ends of the criss-cross sticky tape on the glass are stuck properly.

Actually, my Dad fixed most of the curtains already as well as he could, but the rods aren't quite right and the rings were jamming. So Granpie's up the top taking out screws and re-gimletting holes and so on, and I'm down the bottom handing tools up, and sometimes we swap places to give him a breather, and he tells me what to do.

I know by now that all this is to do with stopping the glass blowing in on us, if there's a war and bombs get dropped. And since yesterday I don't need a newspaper to tell me what's going on, because everyone is listening to the News every time it comes on, and talking about Germany having invaded Poland and things getting serious, and about what may happen, and making sure they know where their own gas-masks are, and that sort of stuff.

But it doesn't seem real. I can't believe in it at all.

Except that everyone's so grim and distant, as if their thoughts are keeping them miles away. Granpie's not even whistling under his breath, and I've never known him not do that when he's working.

All he says is, "Screwdriver, please," or "A bit more to the left," or "Heave that curtain up a bit to take the weight off it," or "That's the ticket, hold the steps steady."

But at last he gives a bit of a smile and says, "That's the finish for now! Off you go out for a bit!"

So I will.

When my brother is not busy working out chess problems he quite likes digging pretend tunnels down the bottom of the garden next to the chickens. Sometimes tunnels, and sometimes earth valleys with wood bridges for toy cars to go over. And I quite like doing it with him.

Unfortunately, Skipper likes helping, too, which doesn't improve matters.

But it's good fun, so I'll do that for a bit.

Perhaps tomorrow things will brighten up.

They didn't.

Granpie and I went round to the Prophets of the Groves' church for eleven o'clock as usual and got settled in the gallery and looked up the hymns. But when the minister came into the pulpit you could tell straight away that something was wrong. He started reading something out and a horrible sort of empty silence fell upon the congregation and I went cold inside.

Then in a sad, heavy but calm voice he said, "Our country is now at war with Germany. Would you stand for the Blessing, and then go quietly to your homes."

And we did. Grown-ups seemed almost cheerful, greeting each other and standing chatting. But I must admit I felt - oh, you know, just blank . . . it was all so very strange, as if some dread thing had happened, like the end of the world.

When we got home, my mother had made a pot of tea and was sitting in the Dining Room with my Dad and my brother and the old ladies, all listening to the wireless and talking. But as soon as Granpie and I joined them, the terrible wailing air-raid siren sounded, going up-and-down and up-and-down, taking your stomach down lower with every wail, and your heart jumping higher and higher in your throat, and you thought, "This is War!"

237

We all froze, when it started, and put cups down, and said nothing. Then my father leapt up and closed the heavy curtains and my mother fetched all the gas-mask boxes and gave them out, and Miss Elphin and Mrs Ritchie (the others must have been away out) and the five of us sat saying nothing in the dark room, with the little boxes on our knees, waiting to be bombed.

But nothing happened. The All Clear went, curtains were opened, the sun streamed in and everything went back to being more normal than it has been for weeks. In fact, they were all happier than I've ever seen them . . . even laughing and joking!

How odd!

My mother, though, was still looking rather thoughtful, but then she smiled round on us all and said, "Well, at least we know where we are, now!"

The grown-ups nodded and smiled back. Even Miss Elphin smiled for a second, and then said moanily to my Mum, "I *am* so glad we've you to look after us," but little old Mrs Ritchie said perkily, "And *I'm* glad we've a nice strong boarding-house to be safe in!" and trotted off to her room, humming, *Keep the Home Fires Burning*!

My Mum hid a smile, but Granpie looked at her with a grave expression. "You, and the boarding-house . . ." he said as he got up to go, " . . . we may live to be very thankful for both."

He picked up his hat briskly and stumped off down the Hall, smiling to himself, and happily whistle-breathing *Guide-Me-O-Thou*.

I don't think I'll ever understand grown-ups.

And I think I shall hate having to be one.

Never mind, there's always school. Nothing can change that, no matter what.

And . . . there is this *ALL* . . .

POSTSCRIPT

I think maybe you have seen through my deception. You're right . . . that was not written when I was eleven, nor twelve. But if a thousand ages in His sight are like an evening gone, what is half a century between friends?

I am still the Child I was.

I'd like to honour them and remember them as they were, my parents and grandparents, for their own sakes and because of what came after.

But most of all I want to remember being a Child, in case I ever stop being one.